THE LORE OF SHIPS

TRE TRYCKARE

CRESCENT BOOKS ◖ NEW YORK

III

Copyright © MCMLXIII
by Tre Tryckare, E. Cagner

This edition published by
CRESCENT BOOKS
a division of Crown Publishers, Inc.
by arrangement with
Tre Tryckare AB.
a b c d e f g h

Library of Congress Catalog
Card Number:
63-18428

TRE TRYCKARE AB
Gothenburg, Sweden.
B7US20733
Printed in Great Britain, 1973.

Acknowledgments

The Lore of Ships has been designed by Tre Tryckare, Cagner & Co., and is based on the ideas and plans of EWERT CAGNER.

The chief of the Editing department, BENGT KIHLBERG, DGI, DIHR, has been the supervising editor of this work. CURT STURE GÖRMAN, DGI, DIHR, head of the Art department, has supervised the graphic design. The illustrations have been hand-lithographed in the Reproduction department at Tre Tryckare under the direction of PER NIELSEN.

Experts from a number of countries have been associated with Tre Tryckare, so that this book is the result of complete international co-operation.

Sea Captain SAM SVENSSON, internationally known maritime expert, has been the chief adviser. He has participated from the planning stage to completion of the book, and has consulted with the many experts concerned. Captain Svensson has checked illustrations and texts and is the author of the Introduction and the commentaries, *Spars and Rigging* and *The Sail*. Formerly curator at the Maritime-Historical Museum in Stockholm, Sweden, Captain Svensson was later engaged in helping to salvage and restore the Swedish warship, Wasa, sunk in 1628 in Stockholm harbor.

WILLIAM A. BAKER, American naval architect, is an expert on historical and modern shipbuilding. He is no doubt best known for his connection with the reconstruction of the *Mayflower*. Mr. Baker has assisted in checking texts as well as illustrations, and is the author of the commentary for *The Hull*.

TAGE BLUM, an engineer and shipbuilding teacher at the Polytechnic Institute, Copenhagen, Denmark, wrote the commentary for *Propulsion*.

GEORG TIMMERMANN, an engineer as well as head of the Maritime and Fishing Section at the Altonaer Museum in Hamburg, Germany, wrote the commentary for the chapter on *Fishing*.

GEORGE P. B. NAISH, Lieutenant Commander and Assistant Keeper at the National Maritime Museum in London, England, did the commentary, *Yachting*.

ALAN W. H. PEARSALL, M.A. and Assistant Keeper at the National Maritime Museum in London, England, is responsible for the commentary on *Gunnery*.

ROLF SCHEEN, Naval Captain in the Norwegian Marines,

author of the commentary introducing *Navigation and Ship-Handling*.

The following writers and experts have also contributed to the book:

P. Å. BERG, Engineer, Chalmer's College of Technology; S. CARLSSON, Editor; Commander H. FORSHELL R. SW. N.; Captain O. R. LILJEQVIST R. SW. N. R.; Å. LINDHOLM, Engineer, Chalmer's College of Technology; Captain S. NOTINI R. SW. N. R.; director of the Maritime Museum of Göteborg; and Commander K. WOLLTER R. SW. N. R.

Extensive work, such as preparatory studies, sketches, and drawings — serving as basic material for most of the illustrations — has been carried out by GORDON MACFIE, artist, Stockholm; and ÅKE GUSTAVSSON, artist, and others in the Art department of Tre Tryckare. Some sketches have also been done by WOLFGANG SELL of Hamburg, Germany.

Original drawings were made by BENGT BERGLUND, RUNE BÅGMARK, BIRGIT DAHLSTRAND, SIV ENGLUND, VERA FAHLSTRÖM, JOHAN LINDSTRÖM, JOSE LLOBETT JUAN, FRITZ ROHDE, LARS-ERIK STRÖM, RUNE SVENSSON, among others.

For checking design, illustrations, and texts in the course of the preparation of the book, Tre Tryckare wishes to thank the following individuals and institutions:

JOHN MUNDAY and other experts at the National Maritime Museum in London, England; HOWARD CHAPELLE, Curator for the Division of Transportation at the Smithsonian Institute, Washington, D.C.; Director SVEIN MOLAUG and Curator ERIK VEA at the Norwegian Maritime Museum in Oslo, Norway; Captain HELMUT GRUBBE, Lübeck-Travemünde; W. STEPHENS, yacht designer, London, England; and B. BOTHEN, engineer, yacht designer, SYR, Göteborg, Sweden.

Gratitude is also due to the following for advice and material.

The Royal British Navy; The Royal Danish Navy; The Royal Swedish Navy; The United States Navy; Arkeologiska Museet (The Archaeological Museum), Göteborg, Sweden; Chalmers Tekniska Högskolas Bibliotek (Library of Chalmer's College of Technology), Göteborg, Sweden; Göteborgs Universitetsbibliotek (Library of the University of Göteborg), Sweden; National Maritime Museum, London, England; Norsk Sjöfartsmuseum (Norwegian Maritime Museum), Oslo, Norway; Sjöfartsmuseet i Göteborg (The Maritime Museum at Göteborg), Göteborg, Sweden; Statens Sjöhistoriska Museum (Maritime-Historical Museum), Stockholm, Sweden; ASEA, Västerås, Sweden; AB. Bofors, Sweden; C.A. Clase AB., Göteborg, Sweden; De Danske Statsbaner (The State Railways of Denmark); Decca Navigator and Radar AB., Göteborg, Sweden; Deutsche Bundesbahn (The State Railways of West Germany), Hamburg, Germany; AB. Electrolux, Stockholm, Sweden; Japanese Embassy, Stockholm, Sweden; Eriksbergs Mek. Verkstads AB., Göteborg, Sweden; AB. Götaverken, Göteborg, Sweden; Kalvin & Hughes Ltd., Göteborg, Sweden; Kockums Mek. Verkstads AB., Malmö, Sweden; AB. Lindholmens Varv, Göteborg, Sweden; Merriman Bros., Inc., Boston, Massachusetts; Motor Boating, New York, New York; Sasebo Heavy Industries Co., Ltd., Tokyo, Japan; Sparkman & Stephens, Inc., New York, New York; Statens Järnvägar (The State Railways of Sweden), Stockholm and Göteborg; Svenska Seglarförbundet, Stockholm, Sweden; AB. Volvo Penta, Göteborg, Sweden; Yachting Publishing Corporation, New York, New York.

THE LORE OF SHIPS

PREFACE

Water has lured the heart of man all of his days — whether it was the silvery line of a river, the gilded sparkle of a lake, or the phosphorescing green glint in an ocean. Angry or calm, fresh or salt, helpful — in giving man his food — or cruel — in bringing him an enemy — the sea makes its presence always known to humans.

Man has depended on it for food, for sport, for transportation. From the moment an ancient man first used the water — perhaps floating down a river holding to a log — when he developed primitive dugout canoes, rafts, barges and sailing ships, liners and tankers, and atomic submarines and surface ships, man has needed the sea. And during this slow, and often painful, evolution, man has tried to conquer the vastness of the oceans. The Lore of Ships illustrates man's fascination with the sea and gives him a chance to satisfy — at least partly — his love of ships and shipping. It is an illustrated book which shows, by means of simplified illustration and detailed drawing, the most important parts of the construction, equipment, and development of all kinds of ships. An explanatory, numbered text allows the reader to follow the diagrams of rigging, sail, engines, spars, fishing, flags — even the weapons used aboard ships through the ages. Each of the chapters begins with a short introduction to the developments that took place in the various subdivisions of nautical history. For example, the first chapter, called "The Hull," explains each part of the evolution of this structure, from its initial appearance covered with animal skin or tree bark to the refined and sophisticated hulls of today's sleek atomic ships. Illustrated details — the basic structure, rudders, steering gears, anchors, and many others — make it easy for the reader to ground himself thoroughly in the lore of the hull.

The technical editors of The Lore of Ships include a curator of a maritime museum, a naval architect, engineers, sea captains, and many more. The book was produced under the expert guidance of captain Sam Svensson, internationally known maritime expert. Dictionary, survey, illustrated book — The Lore of Ships is most of all for the enjoyment of those who would go down to the sea in ships.

TRE TRYCKARE

Contents

and here on the jib-boom I could look at the ship as at a separate vessel — and there rose up from the water, supported only by the small black hull, a pyramid of canvas spreading out far beyond the hull, and towering up almost, as it seemed in the indistinct night-air, to the clouds. The sea was as still as an inland lake; the light trade-wind was gently and steadily breathing from astern; the dark blue sky was studded with the tropical stars: there was no sound but the rippling of the water under the stem: and the sails were spread out, wide and high; — the two lower studding-sails stretching, on each side, far beyond the deck; the top-mast studding-sails, like wings to the topsails; the top-gallant studding-sails spreading fearlessly out above them; still higher, the two royal studding-sails, looking like two kites flying from the same string; and, highest of all, the little skysail, the apex of the pyramid, seeming actually to touch the stars, and to be out of reach of human hand. So quiet, too, was the sea, and so steady the breeze, that if these sails had been sculptured marble, they could not have been more motionless. Not a ripple upon the surface of the canvas; not a quivering of the extreme edges of the sail — so perfectly were they distended by the breeze.

12

PICTORIAL CONTENTS

THE ILLUSTRATIONS ON THESE PAGES IDEN-
TIFY DETAILS FOR READERS WHO DO NOT
KNOW THE NAMES OF CERTAIN PARTS OF THE
SHIP. NUMBERS REFER TO THE PAGES WHERE
THE DETAILS CAN BE FOUND. IT MUST BE KEPT
IN MIND THAT THIS IS A GENERAL SURVEY
AND NOT EVERY ITEM IS INCLUDED.

The text on page 10
is a quotation from one
of the classics of
nautical literature, Two
Years Before The Mast
by Richard Henry
Dana, who went to
sea because his poor
health had compelled
him to interrupt his
law studies. His
description of his
experience at sea is
contained in one of
the finest and most
authentic books ever
written about life on
shipboard. The book
was first published
in 1834.

INTRODUCTION

BY SAM SVENSSON

From ancient times sailing the seas has been a unique profession, with techniques and methods which have always puzzled the landlubber. One thousand years before Christ, Solomon said that the way of a ship in the midst of the sea was too wonderful for him to understand.

In our time there have been radical technical developments. On the seas, ships as well as the life of the sailor has been changed to such a degree that no similarity whatsoever with the olden days exists. This may be why general interest in old nautical things and in the sailing ship in particular has grown to such an extent. People all over the world now want accurate data about the construction, equipment, and handling of old ships.

Long ago, ships were always built of wood, except in the case of even more primitive materials such as reed, skin, and bark; but these materials were only used for the most primitive sailing in narrow seas. Since ancient times ships have been built according to two methods: carvel and clinker. The first method was developed in the eastern Mediterranean countries, where Egyptians, Phoenicians, and others built ships with outside planking ingeniously joined by being placed edge to edge. This art came into general use in Southern Europe, and during the Middle Ages it spread along the coast of Western Europe, reaching the Baltic during the latter part of the 15th century. It then became the dominant way of shipbuilding, and after the middle of the 16th century all large vessels were carvel-built.

During the latter half of the 17th century, however, when shipbuilding had become a science and ships could, theoretically, be constructed in advance, larger and sturdier ships were being built. The pictures on pages 32 and 40 show constructional details of a large 18th-century ship. During the second half of the 19th century, when iron and steel were being used more generally for shipbuilding, fewer wooden ships were being constructed. Yet, these wooden ships were still used chiefly in the United States, where large wooden merchant sailing vessels were built up to the time of the First World War. The four-masted bark Roanoke—3,439 gross tons, built in

1892—and the six-masted schooner, Wyoming—3,730 tons, built in 1909—indicate the size limits of wood used in constructing ships. In many other places, perhaps mostly in the Eastern Mediterranean and in the Near East, but also in the Baltic, small sailing vessels were built of wood as late as the early years of the 20th century. In addition to carvel-built wooden ships, clinker-built vessels were also being constructed. This method originated in the Baltic where, even during the Viking Age, large clinker-built ships sailed to Iceland and Greenland. In the Middle Ages the clinker-building method was predominant in Northern Europe, and many large ships were constructed. Perhaps one of the largest was Henry IV's ship Grace Dieu, built in 1418; she was almost fifty meters long and about twelve meters wide. She had a complicated treble-clinker planking. According to the clinker method, the planking was built first and the frames were inserted afterward. We know this because the wreck of the Grace Dieu was discovered near Southampton, and showed that the rivets of the skin were clinched underneath the frames.

Experimental ships of iron were built during the first half of the 19th century, until, gradually, iron came into more general use. After 1850, England had several shipyards which built only iron vessels. The introduction of the steam engine for propulsion also encouraged the use of iron as a shipbuilding material. The first iron ships were built according to the same principles as those used for wooden vessels, but as builders grew more experienced, special methods were adopted for the structure of iron ships. One early change was to provide the iron steamship with a double bottom and internal keel, instead of the former bar keel used in sailing vessels. The keelson was now placed on top of the floors. Longitudinal framing, which slowly came into use around 1900, also deviated from the kind of standard shipbuilding that had been used for a thousand years.
Electric welding, which was used experimentally on a large scale for German pocket battleships built between the two World Wars, has now completely revolutionized all shipbuilding techniques. Many large ships are now built in sections according to highly specialized methods on the principle of the assembly line. As yet we cannot

determine the extent of this development. The most up-to-date shipyards have the facilities to build and equip a ship from the first steps to the point where it is ready for the sea.

The steam engine and later the diesel engine have only been in existence for a very short time in the whole history of navigation. During most of this time, masts and sails were the only means of propulsion on long voyages. For ages, rigging consisted of one mast and one sail only, and it was not until the end of the Middle Ages that mechanical progress made it possible to construct better and more functional rigging. These developments continued for several centuries and reached their high point after the middle of the 19th century, when, due to competition from the steamship, shipyards turned out perfectly sparred and rigged sailing ships.

There have been many important phases in the history of rigging: such as setting a topsail above the original single square sail, using fidded topmasts that could be sent down, the footrope and the jackstay, which together revolutionized the work of handling sails, the introduction of wire, first for the standing rigging and then for the running gear, and, finally, mechanical aids for handling sails in large ships, such as patent sheaves and brace-and-halliard winches. The introduction of the auxiliary engine with a propeller has, on the other hand, nothing to do with the improvement in sailing vessels.

Flags are not only decorative but also useful. Originally, flags come from field banners carried in ancient battles. In comparison with the flags of ancient kings and military commanders, our national flags are of very recent date. The oldest national flag now in use is the Danish flag, according to a legend of 1219, and was probably followed by the Swedish and Dutch flags. Among the flags of world powers, America has the oldest, dating in its present general form of stars and stripes from 1777. The French tricolor is dated 1794; the English flag in its present form is from 1801.

Page 136 shows the flags used by some of the old sailing ship companies. Perhaps Hansan's red-and-white flag of the Middle Ages should come as number one on this list. On page 137 there are flags that are still in use by shipping companies known all over the world today.

Once the oar had been invented, there were very early attempts to find some mechanical aid which could move ships in a calm or drive them against a head wind. There was no mechanical power. Thus, it was not until the steam engine was invented and perfected to some degree that steam navigation got under way. The first ships of this type were used for river traffic in the United States, and also for coastal traffic around the British Isles.

Steady improvements in the design of the steam engine contributed to the more widespread use of steam navigation. The engine was given several cylinders and was fitted with a condenser. The boilers had forced draft, superheaters, and oil fueling. Finally, the reciprocal steam engine was replaced by a steam turbine, which is frequently used today in very large ships.

In the years just preceding the First World War, attempts were made to use diesel motors as marine engines. Right from the start they appeared to have certain advantages: they had less weight and required less space both for the engine and the bunker. As the reliability of the diesel increased, more motor-driven ships were used throughout the world. In this respect the Scandinavian countries have been in the lead, for example, Sweden's merchant navy consists almost exclusively of motor-driven ships.

Deep-sea fishing is fun, but it is also an important means of getting food. Of old, deep-sea fishing was always carried out in fishing craft fitted with sails. Well-known examples of such craft are the English fishing smacks on the North Sea banks and the American schooners on the Newfoundland coast. Today, both large and small fishing boats are motor-driven, the catch is well taken care of, and there are some factory ships where the catch is cleaned and prepared and then canned or deep-frozen right on board. The most important methods of fishing are line fishing and fishing where a large net is dragged along the sea bed. Now, floating trawls are also used to catch fish on the surface. These trawls are towed by two boats, and the method is more effective than the ordinary drift net. Modern fishing vessels are equipped with echo sounders for locating shoals of fish.

Sailing as a sport has an old heritage. Caligula had pleasure boats in Lake Nemi, and the Doge of Venice had a luxurious galley which he used every year in the ceremony of marrying himself to the sea. In ancient times pleasure sailing was a sport reserved for kings and men of rank only. During the 19th century, it began to occupy more industrialists and businessmen, and, gradually, sailing as a sport has reached the widespread popularity of our own time. Today, there are yacht clubs in all countries where there is access to navigable waters. In order to standardize rules for yachting competitions a great many so-called one-design boats have been constructed, boats which are built according to accurate measurements and regulations so that they will be exactly alike; thus it will be mostly the skill of the helmsman that decides the race. Pages 192 and 193 show many such internationally registered one-design boats. Yacht-racing courses are also decided according to an international standard. Figure C on page 194 shows the fixed track used for all Olympic sailing contests.

As long as man has sailed the ocean, he has struggled for supremacy on the sea. Even in ancient times, a variety of ships were built specifically for war or trade; nevertheless, merchant ships have been used in war and warships in commerce down through the years. As the nations were industrialized, diversity according to function became more noticeable. While today's merchant ships and warships differ in design, there are also various differences in a single category. Warships for both offensive and defensive combat are steadily being altered and improved. Mines, torpedoes, pom-pom guns, and tracer projectiles are standard equipment. Radar and data-processing machines are employed by naval forces; and submarines are fitted with underwater missiles.

It might be said that navigation is the sailor's theory and seamanship his practice. The sounding lead is the sailor's oldest instrument; recognition of the coastline his only way of piloting. In deep waters and when land was out of sight this simple method of navigation was useless. Before the compass was invented, the sailor had to find his way by observations that would indicate a definite direction: the movement of the sun and stars, the direction of the wind and how the clouds were drifting, changes in ocean swell, the flight of birds and how the fish swam. On a long voyage not even the compass was a sufficient guide, so that such trips could not be undertaken until astronomic navigation had been discovered. Even then, for hundreds of years the only means by which a sailor could measure the sun's meridian height was with a simple instrument which determined latitude. The ability to make longitudinal calculations came at a much later date. For that purpose the navigator required Hadley's octant or a sextant, as well as a chronometer and complete nautical tables, or if there were no chronometer, he had to be able to calculate the longitude by means of lunar distances. As in other fields, electronics now does most of the work formerly done by astronomic navigation.

Previously, seamanship could be defined as the care and handling of sailing ships. Page 250 illustrates a portion of this almost forgotten art: how a brig can be put to sea against the wind by backing and filling downriver. Today, a vessel is guided by means of the rudder and the screw. To maneuver a large power-driven vessel properly differs vastly from the skillful handling of a large sailing ship. The art of guiding a power-driven vessel has been mastered by many of today's seamen, but skill in sailing is rarely to be found. *The Lore of Ships* has tried to recover some small part of this forgotten art.

*The first chapter of
The Lore of Ships
deals with the hull and
some of its more
important details. The
next page shows a
sketch of Columbus'
ship, the* SANTA MARIA.

THE HULL

BY WILLIAM A. BAKER

Throughout history hull shapes have been dictated by the type of construction, mode of propulsion, use, fashion, and whim. Primitive craft ranged from round shapes — woven baskets, skin-covered framework, and even pottery — to the long and narrow, such as bundles of reeds and shaped logs. The most widespread form of hull was the log canoe, which was quickly improved by the addition of one or more planks to each side. For centuries, built-up hulls followed the general shape of such canoes.

The continued existence of primitive forms points to the fact that the main development of ships occurred in the Mediterranean region and in northern Europe. Shipbuilding history is in the main concerned with wooden sailing ships, since metal ships and mechanical propulsion occur in only the later years of the recorded history of shipbuilding. Through most of this time there was a parallel development of the two forms noted above: the "round" ship, or bulky cargo carrier, and the "long" ship which was built for speed.

The design of early ships was influenced by the type of tools then available. Northern shipbuilders, for instance, used an adze to shape one plank from each half of a felled tree. These planks were lapped at the edges and fastened by lacings (later by metal rivets) — the present day clinker planking. Once the planking was secured, the framing was inserted and lashed into place to lugs that had been left on the planks during the original shaping. The main strength of such vessels came from the long, edge-lapped planking.

Southern builders, on the other hand, had the saw with which to produce several planks from each log. These were fastened edge to edge — smooth planking now called carvel-building. Ancient Egyptian shipbuilders were plagued by a shortage of wood suitable for shipbuilding, and so they had to develop ingenious dowels and key-pieces to hold their short planks of acacia wood together. The Egyptian ships were basically river boats, built without a structural keel but with a thick plank in its place. These boats were frameless double-enders and had arc form midsections. Heavy rope trusses, fitted from bow to stern, assisted in keeping these weak ships from sagging at the ends. Eventually, heavy framing was added to seagoing vessels to supplement and strengthen the plank edge fastenings, thus eliminating the rope truss. The strength of Southern vessels came from the framing, that of Northern ships from the planking, and it was this essential difference that determined the basic features of Northern and Southern ships up to the time of the Crusades.

Available information indicates that Mediterranian vessels of the Greek and Roman eras were basically double-enders and that their builders had a sound knowledge of structure. Naturally curved timbers formed the framing and nail-fastened scarf joints were used as needed. The Romans used three kinds of vessels: chubby sailing merchantmen, stout warships propelled by oars and used for ramming, and light speedy galleys for carrying messages and transporting important personages.

From Roman times to about 1200 A.D. there was little change in Southern ships. With the slight alteration of lower ends, merchant hulls remained the same as the Roman double-ender with a rather full stern and steering oars. Deck beams, secured to a heavy wale, protruded through the carvel planking, and "castles," which were not part of the hull, were fixed prominently on bow and stern — the square work of house carpenters contrasting with the curved work of the shipwrights. An important change took place when the Roman square rig was replaced by the two- or three-masted lateen rig. From the Greek and Roman multi-banked triremes, "long" ships now returned to the single bank of oars. These galleys were fitted with and occasionally used sail when the winds were favorable.

Experts do not agree on the origin of the Northern Viking ship, one school believing it developed from the log canoe to which planks were added; others saying it emanated from skin boats where thin planks had replaced the sewn skins on a flexible framework. Page 26 shows what may be the final phase of lashed-on planking: the midsection of the famous Gokstad ship, *circa* 900 A.D. Only the lower eight planks are lashed to the frames; the remainder are nailed.

From 1095, the time of the first Crusade, the features of Northern and Southern "round" ships began to be mingled. Superstructures were added in the North, along with other details; while Southern shipbuilders adopted the stern rudder and returned to the square rig. The standard type which resulted, commonly called the cog, was used from the Mediterranean to the Baltic until the early 1400's. The cog's hull was still basically of the double-ended type. Its stem was raked forward and was usually strongly curved, while the slightly raked sternpost was straight in order to take the rudder. The fo'c'sle was triangular in plan, projecting over the bow, but its after end was partially faired into the hull. The after castle remained an angular house. Still, there was a difference between Northern and Southern cogs: in the North cogs had clinker planking, a few projecting tie beams, and decks supported generally inside the hull; while in the

South they had smooth planking with all deck beam ends protruding.

Seagoing ships grew larger during the 15th century, and Northern builders began to realize there was a limit to the size of successful clinker-built ships. With the improvement of shipbuilding technique, the projecting deck beam and tie beam ends, which were difficult to keep tight, were abandoned. In general, the European ship combined a number of features: smooth planking on heavy framing plus inside supported decks. It is almost impossible today to describe accurately the types of ship that followed the cog, such ships as the galleass, galliot, and galleon, deriving from oar-propelled craft, and the caravel, carrack, and hulk, the pure sailing vessels.

During the 15th and 16th centuries the appearance of the ship's hull above water changed considerably. Castles remained large but lost their angular look and were merged into the main hull. Around 1550 large ships adopted a square stern that gave better support to the superstructure. About the same time, the fo'c'sle lost its triangular form; and its projection was dropped to form a beakhead below the bowsprit in imitation of the galley ram. The major ship type for the next 75 to 100 years was the galleon, which had less sheer and lower superstructure than earlier types and was longer for its breadth. In the 17th century there was a considerable change in framing details. Up to the late 16th century, the single frame of several naturally curved pieces with scarfed joints had been used for large ships; but such joints were weak and improvements were effected by shifting the pieces so that they overlapped each other side by side for several feet. The lowest pieces were nearly square and were spaced along the keel about their own thickness apart. In way of the laps there was nearly solid timber for the length of the ship, but the pieces were not fastened together. By the early 18th century the pieces had been extended to butt against each other and were fastened together to form a complete frame that could be erected as a unit. This is essentially the pattern of framing still employed in the building of large wooden ships.

Radical changes in the underwater forms of ships came in the 18th and 19th centuries. The rough semicircular shape of the log canoe has been discussed, but builders soon learned that flattening the bottom of this shape could improve stability. This development would, in general, be a simple description of the midsection shape of practically all vessels until the early part of the 18th century. The unique V-shaped Viking section remained but a local feature.

The earliest shipbuilding treatises and ship plans preserved date from the early 1400's, and indicate a long tradition of ship design using arcs of circles and their derivatives. Succeeding works amplified the details and show that ship proportions and parts were defined in terms of keel length or breadth, usually the latter; that vessels for fast sailing differed in relation of length to breadth rather than in the shape of the sections. In 1750, and perhaps even later, it was still possible to design a satisfactory ship with no tools but a pair of compasses and a straight-edge.

About 1670 the results of what was perhaps the first systematic ship resistance experiments were recorded in England. Other scientific studies followed, particularly in France, where the first stability treatise was published in 1746. Yet during this period there was little real progress in improving the form of ships. Even up to the beginning of the 19th century it was difficult to distinguish between merchant ships and warships, except, of course, the multi-decked ships of the line. Before the introduction of iron knees and strapping the building of long wooden ships was virtually impossible, for the structure was too elastic. This elasticity required that warships have full lines at the ends to support the armament carried there, and as warships set the pattern so the merchant ships followed.

In the 18th century many legal and extra-legal businesses required the use of small fast-sailing vessels, like those built in Bermuda and the Chesapeake Bay area. The phrases Virginia-built or Virginia-model became almost synonymous with speed. Later on, this type was known as the Baltimore clipper, a feature of which was a return to the V-shaped bottom of the Viking ship, the so-called rising floor, which was gradually adopted for large ships wherever speed was more important than carrying capacity.

A trans-Atlantic packet line, which began in 1816, brought a demand for speed in large ships. The first packet ships were similar to naval frigates — handy flush-decked vessels, though far from fine-lined. Later ships were of a flat-floored type, developed for the New Orleans cotton trade, with sections similar to those of modern cargo ships. Actually, their reputation for speed was due more to the driving power of their captains than to any quality of form.

The Baltimore clipper was also adapted for the East India and China trade, where sailing ability in light winds was more necessary than capacity for bulky cargoes. The large, extreme clipper lasted as a type from about 1845 to 1860, and was developed out of a rising fashion for speed and publicity. Successful clippers were built with both flat and rising floors, but few had the hollow water lines popularly associated with this type, the average being more like those shown on pages 22 and 23. The speeds of clipper ships were again largely the result of driving made possible by their size, but economic necessity finally forced a return to the best of the packet forms, ships nearly as fast but capable of carrying more cargo.

Around 1600 elaborate stern and quarter galleries, side carvings, and large figureheads were introduced to decorate large merchant and warships. By 1800 these were reduced to some stern windows, small quarter galleries, and relatively simple head structures. During these same two centuries, superstructures were reduced until even the fo'c'sle and the poop were hidden by a continuous sheer line. In the last days of sail, ships were decorated with only simple figureheads and perhaps a scroll or two on the stern.

The introduction of steam propulsion brought new problems to the shipbuilder: the weight of machinery and the strains induced by paddle wheels or the screw propellers. Until around 1870 ocean-going steamships followed the form and construction of the sailing ship, and carried large sailing rigs, until steam propulsion eventually became more reliable.

Steamboats for inland waters, particularly in North America, were a different problem. Employed mainly in speedy passenger services, displacement and draft were small, and to stiffen their lightly built hulls the old Egyptian truss in the form of a structural frame was often used.

By the middle of the 19th century it had been determined, through further resistance experiments and practical experience with steam, that fine lines were necessary for speed. A sailing ship could increase sail in order to overcome poor lines, but early propelling machinery was very limited in application and breakdowns were frequent, with occasional disastrous results. Although iron parts had been used on wooden ships as far back as 1675, commercial iron shipbuilding did not start until the 1830's. Early practice was to have an iron part similar to every wooden part, as shown on page 30. Many shipowners were prejudiced against iron, and so before it could be fully adopted there was the interim phase of the composite ship, in which iron framing and tie plates were used with wood planking and decking, as shown on page 27.

As builders gained experience it was found that the longitudinal material could be distributed to better advantage than in the old wooden ships, where the theory was that the keel was the backbone and provided most of the strength. It was soon realized that a metal ship should be built as a girder with as much strength in the deck as in the bottom. This, of course, is modern shipbuilding practice. Steel, which is now practically the universal material in all large ships, was first used to replace iron around 1870.

The use of iron and steel in shipbuilding has provided designers and builders with practically limitless possibilities. Almost any conceivable shape can be obtained, and while riveted joints offered certain problems, the general introduction of electric welding in the 1930's eliminated many difficult joints. Large sections of ships can now be assembled in convenient locations and placed in position on the building ways by cranes.

Modern ship forms are the result of countless towing-tank and full-scale experiments. Today a model is usually tested for each new design. While not as readily apparent as formerly, there are still differences between ship shapes according to the service performed; one need only compare an oil tanker with a fast passenger liner to see the modern versions of the "round" and "long" ships.

One can now look forward to using new forms and materials: ships on water-borne wings and on air cushions indicate one direction; semi-submerged and fully submerged forms indicate the other. Chemicals and glass fibers are used for the hull construction of smaller boats and the size of these is now approaching 100 feet. Light metals are being widely applied where weight reduction is important. Yet wood, the ancient standard, cut into thin layers or small pieces, glued, chemically treated, and formed into shapes, cannot be discounted in the building of ships.

PROFILE OF A WOODEN SAILING SHIP, 1864.

This semi-clipper ship was constructed in 1862 by Niels Kierkegaard, naval architect and Master Shipwright at the Old Shipyard in Gothenburg. In 1864 he published a handbook on naval architecture which *contained drawings of eighteen different ships, including this one. His example was followed by shipbuilders all over Scandinavia. The ship shown here has concave bows with narrow waterlines* *and a lean run under the transom counter and surmounting square stern. She was rigged as a bark, as indicated by the three shrouds and single backstay in the mizzen rigging and shown by the chain* *plates. All the chain plates are bolted flat to the side of the ship without any channels. They go through the main rail, so the deadeyes will be located inside the topgallant bulwark. The fore and main rigging* *has four lower shrouds, two topmast backstays, one topgallant backstay, and one royal backstay, as indicated by the chain plates. This same ship is shown on the next two pages.*

PROFILE OF A WOODEN SAILING SHIP, 1864

1 Sternpost	6 Headpiece	11 Sheer strake	16 Rudder	21 Figurehead
2 Keel	7 Garboard strake	12 Covering board	17 Counter	22 Mizzenmast
3 False keel or shoe	8 Bottom planking	13 Bulwark	18 Stern	23 Mainmast
4 Fore foot, gripe	9 Side planking	14 Rough-tree rail	19 Chain plates	24 Foremast
5 Stem	10 Wale	15 Topgallant bulwark	20 Cathead	25 Bowsprit

A

B

C

D

LINES OF A WOODEN SAILING SHIP OF 500 TONS DWT, 1864

The shape of the hull is determined by three sets of planes drawn at right angles to each other. Horizontal planes are called water lines, where they intersect the hull. They are shown as straight lines in A

and as curves in B. WL indicates the load water line. Vertical planes going fore and aft and parallel to the longitudinal middle-line plane are called buttocks. Their intersec-tions with the ship's hull are shown in A as curved lines, marked X, XI, and X2. Vertical planes going across the hull show the curves of the sides of the ship's transverse frame lines. Their shape is given

tions with the ship's hull are shown in A as curved lines, marked X, XI, and X2. Vertical planes going across the hull show the curves of the sides of the ship's transverse frame lines. Their shape is given

in the body plan on page 22, which shows an end view of the hull. The frame lines are numbered in the afterbody and lettered in the forebody. The body plan also gives the diagonal

lines extending from the middle-line plane. The diag-onal intersections with the surface of the hull are drawn on page 23 in C. 23. D above gives the deck plan: three hatches, a fo'c'sle for 10 sailors, galley, and sail locker in

the deckhouse, while the cabinhouse holds the cap-tain's cabin, the mates' rooms, saloon, messroom, and pantries. The little house furthest aft holds the lamp locker and the officers' lavatory.

THE LINES OF A SHIP

A *Body Plan*
B *Sheer Plan*
C *Half Breadth Plan*

The shape of a ship is fully determined by three different systems of planes intersecting the molded surface of a ship's hull and drawn at right angles to each other.

Vertical sections going athwartship give the shape of the frames, as shown in red on the body plan. They are numbered from the sternpost forward. The distance between the first and last gives the length of the ship on her load water line, which equals the length between perpendiculars.

Sections drawn horizontally are called water lines, and are seen in brown on the half breadth plan, C. They are numbered from the bottom of the ship, which is the Base Line. One water line corresponds with the calculated Load Water Line, which is water line number six in this drawing. Vertical sections going fore and aft parallel with the middle line are called buttocks. They are shown in their true form as light brown lines on the sheer plan. They are marked in Roman numerals.

Besides all these lines, the shape of the hull is controlled by diagonal sections; only one is shown on the body plan. Such diagonal planes intersect the shell plating nearly at right angles, and, thus indicate any unfairness that may exist in the molded shape of the hull. The laid off diagonals are shown below the base line in the sheer plan.

The drawing gives one more curve, marked S, using the load water line in the sheer plan as a datum. This curve represents the displacement of the ship. The area of each section below the load water line is represented by a proportional vertical line set off at the corresponding station. Thus the area within the curved line represents the volume of the submerged part of the ship's hull, i.e., her displacement.

On the drawings are:

AP	*After perpendicular*
BL	*Base line*
CL	*Center line*
FP	*Forward perpendicular*
LWL	*Load water line*
D	*Diagonal*
S	*Curve of areas (displacement curve)*
0—20	*Numbers of sections*
WL 1— WL 9	*Water lines*
BI—B III	*Buttock lines*

GENERAL ARRANGEMENT OF A MODERN CARGO SHIP

Shelter-decked ship of 8,200 tons dwt, built by Götaverken, 1961. Class: Lloyd's Register + 100 A 1. Ice class: 3

Dimensions

Length over all: 471'—7⅝"

Length between p.p. as per class: 430'—3"

Breadth molded: 65'—0"

Depth molded to shelter deck, 39'—0"
Depth molded to main deck, 29'—0"
Draft on summer freeboard: 26'—1½"

Machinery:

One six-cylinder, super-charged diesel engine
Two cycle single-acting: 8,950 IHP
Diameter of cylinder: 29.92"

Length of stroke: 59.06"
Revolutions per minute: 112
Diameter of propeller: 16'—10¾"
Pitch of propeller variable: 17'—2½"

The top drawing gives the general appearance of the ship, with principal layout details of the hull. The ship is of the shelter-deck type with fo'c'sle, bridge, and poop. The bridge is separated from the poop by only a narrow well, where the tonnage opening is placed. The ship has five cargo holds, and the number 5

hold is divided into several rooms for chilled cargo. For handling cargo there are four booms and a heavy lift boom at the foremast, two deck cranes between hatches 2 and 3, two samson posts with four booms between hatches 3 and 4, two deck cranes in front of the bridge, and another two cranes for number 5 hold.

Below the profile are three plans of the different decks. The first gives the fo'c'sle head, top of deck-houses, bridge deck, and poop deck. The middle plan shows the shelter deck with the space below the fo'c'sle head, bridge deck, and poop deck. The third plan is the main deck.

MIDSHIP SECTION OF A VIKING SHIP, MIDDLE OF 9TH CENTURY

(After the Gokstad ship)
The ship is clinker-built
and has a deep keel for
sailing. She is undecked,
but has floors fitted
over the frames and
very heavy mast partners
to keep the mast steady.
The gallows could carry
horizontal tent poles.

1 Keel
2 Keelson
3 Floors
4 Futtocks
5 Toptimber
6 Clinker-built skin
7 Flooring
8 Mast partners
9 Riders to keep mast
  partners in place
10 Gallows

Page 27: MIDSHIP SECTION OF TWO DIFFERENT SHIPS, SECOND HALF OF THE 19TH CENTURY

A *Wooden ship*
1 Keel
2 Garboard strake
3 Bottom planking
4 Bends or wales
5 Topside planking
6 Sheer strake
7 Floor
8 2nd futtock
9 4th futtock
10 Long toptimber
11 Limbers, water course
12 Keelson

13 Limber board
14 Limber strake
15 Floor ceiling
16 Thick strakes of
  ceiling
17 Air courses
18 Lower deck hanging
  knee
19 Lower deck shelf
20 Lower deck clamp
21 Hold stanchion

22 Lower deck beam
23 Lower deck, lower
  deck planking
24 Lower deck waterway
25 Lower deck
  spirketing
26 Tween deck ceiling
27 Upper deck hanging
  knee
28 Upper deck shelf
29 Upper deck clamp
30 Tween deck stanchion

Continued

31 Upper deck beam	B *Composite ship*	9 Side intercostal	19 Hold pillar; hold	27 Upper deck pillar,	37 Topgallant bulwark
32 Upper deck, upper	*(wooden vessel with*	keelson	stanchion	upper deck stanchion	stanchion
deck planking	*iron frames)*	10 Center line keelson	20 Lower deck	28 Upper deck	38 Topgallant rail
33 Upper deck waterway	1 False keel or shoe	11 Limber boards	21 Lower deck beam	29 Upper deck beam	39 Deadeye
34 Covering board	2 Keel	12 Ceiling	22 Bracket end (of lower	30 Bracket end (of upper	40 Upper channel
35 Bulwark stanchions	3 Garboard strake	13 Side keelson	deck beam)	deck beam)	41 Bulwark planking
36 Planksheer	4 Keel plate	14 Bilge keelson	23 Lower deck tie plate	31 Upper deck tie plate	42 Chainplate
37 Bulwark planking	5 Frame	15 Bilge plate	24 Lower deck stringer	32 Upper deck stringer	43 Planksheer
38 Main rail	6 Floor	16 Covering board	25 Lower deck waterway	plate	44 Sheer strake
39 Tween decks	7 Limbers	17 Bilge stringer	26 Cargo battens	33 Upper deck waterway	45 Iron sheer strake
40 Hold	8 Reverse frame	18 Cargo battens	(between decks)	34 Covering board	46 Lower channel
		(in hold)		35 Bulwark stanchion	47 Chain bolt
				36 Main rail	48 Preventer bolt

SOME CONSTRUCTION DETAILS OF WOODEN SHIPS, 19TH CENTURY

A *The timbers were placed at right angles to the keel, except at the ends, both fore and aft, where they were placed at right angles to the ship's side. These frames were called cant timbers.*

B *To make the plank strakes run fair, fore and aft, the midship bend (ab) was divided into the same number of planks as the frames (ac) and as at the ends of the ship (ad)*

C *At the ends of the ship, if the planks were too wide, stealers (a) were put in between them; if too narrow, they were formed as joggle planks (b)*

D *Below the water line tree nails (trunnels) and bolts were used to fasten the planking to the frames in addition to two nails in each plank butt*

1 Tree nail
2 Nail
3 Bolt

DETAILS OF A WOODEN VESSEL (FROM PAASCH)

A, B	4 Eking	11 Outside plank	C *Deck and hatchway*	5 Head ledges	12 Mast carlings
Horizontal section of bow	5 Deck hook	12 Ceiling plank	1 Hatch cover	6 Fore and after	13 Chocks
1 Stem	6 Deck hook bolts	13 Breast hook	2 Hatchway	7 Hatch end beams	*(12 and 13 forming mast partners)*
2 Stem rabbet	7 Stem piece	14 Breast hook bolts	3 Hatchway coamings	8 Half beams	14 Mast beams
3 Apron	8 Knight head	15 Deck beam	4 Hatchway carling	9 Lodging knees	15 Deck planking
	9 Hawse timbers			10 Deck stanchions	
	10 Fore cant timbers			11 Mast hole	

INSIDE VIEW OF A RIVETED IRON OR STEEL SHIP WITH SINGLE BOTTOM

1 Keel	8 Bilge keelson	16 Main deck stringer plate	22 Hold pillars or stanchions	28 Bulwark stays	34 Side plating (outside strakes)
2 Floors	9 Bilge stringer	17 Main deck tie plate	23 Bulkhead	29 Spurs (of bulwark stays)	35 Bilge
3 Limber holes	10 Frames	18 Main deck pillars or stanchions	24 Collars	30 Upper sheer strake	36 Bilge strakes
4 Clips	11 Reverse frames	19 Lower deck beams	25 Butt straps	31 Topside strake	37 Bottom plating
5 Center line keelson	12 Upper deck beams	20 Lower deck stringer plate	26 Main rail cap or bulwark cap	32 Main sheer strake	38 Garboard strakes
6 Side keelson	13 Center line deck stringer or girder	21 Lower deck tie plate	27 Bulwark plating	33 Side plating (inside strakes)	
7 Intercostal keelson, side intercostal keelson	14 Upper deck pillars or stanchions				
	15 Main deck beams				

MIDSHIP SECTION OF AN ALL-WELDED DRY CARGO SHIP

1 Shelter deck	8 Bulwark stanchion	16 Bracket or beam knee	22 Bulkhead stiffener	27 Tank top longitudinals	34 Bilge bracket
2 Main deck	9 Stringer plate	17 Main framing	23 Side plating	28 Vertical keel	35 Gusset
3 Second deck	10 Hatch coaming	18 Longitudinal hatch girder	24 Bilge plating	29 Docking brackets	36 Tripping bracket
4 Tank top or inner bottom	11 Stiffener	19 Hatch end pillar	25 Cargo battens	30 Bracket floor	37 Deck beam
5 Bottom plating	12 Border (edging)	20 Hatchway carling	26 Bottom longitudinals	31 Flat keel plate	38 Deck beam
6 Bulwark	13 Hatch beam	21 Longitudinal bulkhead		32 Girder	39 Deck transverse web
7 Freeing port	14 Hatch cover			33 Margin plate	40 Deck longitudinal
	15 Sheer strake				

LONGITUDINAL SECTION OF THE FOREBODY OF A 40-GUN FRIGATE, 1768

1 Keel	6 Stem	11 Head timbers	16 Bitts
2 Floors	7 Apron	12 Head rails	17 Orlop deck beams
3 Keelson	8 Stemson	13 Foremast	18 Gun deck beams
4 Forefoot	9 Bobstay piece	14 Mast step	19 Upper deck beams
5 Gripe	10 Filling chocks	15 Breast hooks	20 Cathead

21 Kevels	26 Mangerboard
22 Knight	27 Shotlocker
23 Jeer capstan	28 Galley wood
24 Galley	29 Bosun's stores
25 Cable	30 Cable tier

THREE-MASTED WOODEN SHIP, 500 TONS DWT, LONGITUDINAL SECTION OF THE FOREBODY

1 False keel or shoe	7 Fore foot	14 Cathead
2 Keel	8 Cutwater piece, gripe	15 Kevel head
3 Floors	9 Stem	16 Pawl bitt
4 Keelson	10 Apron	17 Standard knee
5 Fore deadwood	11 Stemson	18 Pawls
6 Keel scarf	12 Stem knee	19 Pawl rim
	13 Lace piece	20 Windlass barrel

21 Carrick bitt or windlass bitt	27 Fore hatch coaming
22 Mooring bollards	28 Bowsprit
23 Pinrail	29 Foreward bitt
24 Main rail	30 Main deck beams
25 Topgallant rail	31 Tween deck ceiling
26 Port	

32 Main deck diagonal hanging knees
33 Tween deck beams
34 Lower hold ceiling
35 Breast hooks
36 Foremast

OLD CARPENTER'S TOOLS

From a book on shipbuilding, 1691

1 English broad axe
2 Folding rule, a foot and a half long
3 Horse iron with an iron handle
4 Reeming iron
5 Curved caulking iron
6 Carpenter's hatchet
7 Inside calipers
8 Dutch brace and bit
9 Small bevel
10 Crab iron
11 Dutch rule
12 Pair of pincers
13 English auger with a screw
14 Dutch handsaw
15 Big mallet with iron hoops
16 Caulking iron
17 English adze
18 English chisel
19 Gouge
20 Chalk line and reel
21 Draw knife
22 Chisel with a handle

23 Making iron
24 Swedish caulking
   mallet
25 English handsaw
26 Deck scraper
27 Compass saw

28 Swedish chopping axe
29 Compasses with
   crayon
30 Dividers
31 Swedish adze
32 Swedish auger
33 Caulking iron

34 Small gouge to start
   auger holes
35 Grease well to use
   when caulking
36 English maul
37 Spike iron

38 Dutch axe
39 Sledge hammer
40 Rave hook or ripping
   iron for cleaning
   caulking from seams
41 Crab iron, made like a
   clasp knife

42 Adze, as seen from the
   side
43 Crowbar
44 English auger with a
   wooden handle
45 English claw hammer

46 English caulking
   mallet
47 Common hammer
48 Swedish gouge for
   pinewood
49 Reeming iron

FORWARD ELEVATION OF A THREE-DECKED STEAMER, 1900

1 Fo'c'sle deck	8 Deck beams	15 Limber hole	22 Cement filling	29 Chain locker	36 Stem
2 Deck beams	9 Deck pillars	16 Bottom frame	23 Deep floors	30 Horizontal bulkhead	37 Angle clips
3 Deck pillars	10 Lower deck	17 Floor	24 Reverse frame	stiffeners	38 Storeroom above
4 Main deck	11 Deck beams	18 Angle clips	25 Bracket	31 Forepeak bulkhead,	forepeak tank
5 Deck beams	12 Center keelson	19 Center girder	26 Pillars	collision bulkhead	39 Hatch to storeroom
6 Deck pillars	13 Tank top plating	20 Bar keel	27 Beams	32 Vertical bulkhead	above forepeak tank
7 Tween deck	14 Bottom plating	21 Reverse frame	28 Chain locker bulkhead	stiffeners	40 Hawse pipe
				33 Forepeak tank	
				34 Beam	
				35 Breast hooks	

FORE END OF AN ALL-WELDED CARGO SHIP

1 Fo'c'sle deck	6 Bottom plating	12 Transverse deck beam	17 Stringer (strength-ening beam)	22 Watertight flat	27 Watertight floor
2 Shelter deck	7 Bulkhead	13 Longitudinal girder		23 Longitudinal swash	28 Floor
3 Main deck	8 Bulkhead stiffener	14 Transverse web beam	18 Collision bulkhead	plate	29 Bottom longitudinals
4 Second deck	9 Door	15 Main framing	19 Chain locker stiffener	24 Stringer plates	30 Tank top longitudinals
5 Tank top	10 Bulwark	16 Vertical web	20 Chain pipe	25 Intercostal vertical keel	
	11 Bulwark stanchion		21 Chain locker	26 Deep floors	

DETAILS FROM IRON AND STEEL SHIPS

A *Single plate keelson*
B *Box keelson*
C *Intercostal vertical keel*
D *Continuous vertical keel*

A—D
1 Rider plate
2 Vertical plate
3 Inner bottom center line strake
4 Flat plate keel
5 Floors
6 Frames
7 Reverse frames
8 Limber holes

E *Inside view of plating, frames, etc., of an older riveted steel ship*
1 Outside strakes
2 Inside strakes
3 Treble-riveted butt strap
4 Double-riveted butt strap
5 Angle bar stringer on top of reverse frames
6 Frames
7 Reverse frames

F *Single-riveted end lap*
1 Plate
2 Rivet
3 Snap head or button head
4 Rivet shank
5 Driven button head
6 Caulking seam

G *Various kinds of riveting*
1 Pan head, tapered rivet, button point
2 Pan head rivet, countersunk point
3 Button-headed rivet, countersunk point
4 Countersunk head and point

DETAILS FROM IRON AND STEEL SHIPS

A *Various kinds of steel sections*
1 Equal angle bar
2 Unequal angle bar
3 Bulb angle bar
4 Tee bar
5 Channel bar
6 Z-bar
7 I-beam

8 Bulb plate
9 Riveted section formed by two angles and a bulb plate
10 Riveted section formed by four angles and a flat plate

B *Various kinds of riveted frames*
11 Channel
12 Bulb angle
13 Two angles
14 Angle

C *Various kinds of riveting in plating*
1 Joggled outside strakes and flat inside strakes

2 Inside and outside strakes without joggling
3 Clinker built
4 Carvel built

D *Various kinds of keels*
1 Bar keel
2 Flat plate keel

E *Fillet welds*
1 Lap joint
2 T-connection
3 Double continuous weld with scalloped frame
4 Intermittent fillet weld

F *Butt welds*
1 Square weld with gap
2 V-weld without gap
3 U-weld
4 X-weld

G *Slot weld*

LONGITUDINAL SECTION OF THE AFTERBODY OF A 40-GUN FRIGATE, 1768

1 Keel	7 Deadwood	12 Binnacle	18 Poop deck beams	24 Doorway to quarter	29 Salt meat
2 Floors	8 Crutches	13 Mizzenmast	19 Main capstan	gallery	30 Powder room
3 Keelson	9 Rudder	14 Mast step	20 Gunports	25 Wardroom	31 Lantern for powder
4 Sternpost	10 Tiller	15 Orlop deck beams	21 Companion hood	26 Storerooms	room
5 Inner post	11 Wheel	16 Gun deck beams	22 Officer's room	27 Ballast	32 Shot locker
6 Stern knee		17 Upper deck beams	23 Great cabin	28 Water, beer casks	

WL

THREE-MASTED BARK, LONGITUDINAL SECTION OF THE AFTERBODY

1 Keel	6 Keelson scarf	11 Bearding line	16 Cabin house
2 False keel or shoe	7 Stern knee	12 Pinrail	17 Main deck beams
3 Keel scarf	8 After deadwood	13 Main rail	18 Diagonal deck beam
4 Floor	9 Inner post	14 Topgallant bulwark	hanging knees
5 Keelson	10 Sternpost	15 Lamp locker, round-	19 Ceiling
		house	20 Tween deck beams
			21 Crutches
			22 Mizzenmast
			23 Rudder

ANCIENT RUDDERS

A *Rudder of small medie-*
   val ship
1 Main piece of rudder
2 Back piece
3 Head
4 Tiller
5 Pintles
6 Pintle straps
7 Gudgeon straps

B *Rudder arrangement in*
   a Roman merchant ship
   about A. D. 200
1 Stern ornament
2 Helmsmen
3 Tillers

4 Rudder stock
5 Sternpost
6 Carrying ropes
7 Lashing
8 Balcony
9 Rudder blade

C *Rudder of a Dutch*
   fleut, middle of 17th
   century
1 Tiller
2 Pintle straps
3 Rudder braces or
   gudgeon straps
4 Rudder blade
5 Sternpost

D *Rudder arrangement in*
   the Viking era
   about A.D. 850
   (Gokstad ship)
1 Broadside view of
   steering oar
2 Stern view of steering
   oar

3 Tiller
4 Rudder rope
5 Knot
6 "Wart"
7 Tilting rope
8 Collar

RUDDERS

A *Rudder in a wooden*
  sailing ship
1 Rudder blade
2 Tiller
3 Rudder head
4 Rudder stock
5 Pintle straps
6 Pintles
7 Gudgeon straps

B *Iron rudder*
1 Stock of rudder
2 Pintles
3 Rudder frame
4 Heel pintle
5 Rudder plate

C *Steering screws in*
  tunnel to enable
  swinging ship in port
  (sometimes called a
  "Bow-thruster")

D *Contra-guide rudder*
1 Rudder above shaft
  line
2 Sternpost above shaft
  line
3 Sternpost below shaft
  line
4 Rudder below shaft
  line
5 Shaft line

E *Balanced rudder*
1 Stock
2 Rudder
3 Heel of keel

F *Balanced rudder in a*
  twin-screw ship

G *Oertz rudder*
1 Rudder
2 Sternpost

LONGITUDINAL SECTION OF STERN OF AN OLD IRON STEAMER

1 Bulwark	10 Lower deck	18 Tank top	27 Beams	36 Rudder post	45 Rudder stock
2 Bulwark stanchion	11 Deck beams	19 Bar keel	28 Deep floors	37 Gudgeon	46 Cant frames at stern
3 Main deck	12 Deck pillars	20 Floors	29 Propeller blade	38 Rudder arms	47 Rudder quadrant
4 Poop bulkhead	13 Afterpeak bulkhead	21 Limber hole	30 Rope guard	39 Pintle	48 Rudder stock stuffing
5 Deck beams	14 Shaft tunnel or shaft	22 Cement filling	31 Propeller boss	40 Nut	box
6 Deck pillars	alley	23 Propeller shaft	32 Propeller nut cap	41 Portable section for	49 Brackets
7 Tween deck	15 Top of shaft tunnel	24 Stuffing box	33 Stern bearing	better steering in	50 Deck beams of whale-
8 Deck beams	16 Stiffeners on shaft	25 Water outlet pipe	34 Sternpost	restricted waters	back
9 Deck pillars	alley top	26 Afterpeak tank	35 Sole piece	42 Stiffeners	51 Poop
	17 Pedestal of shaft			43 Connecting strap	52 Deck beams
	bearing			44 Bolt	

AFTER END OF AN ALL-WELDED CARGO SHIP

1 Boat deck	10 Transverse deck beams	19 Main framing	28 Stern post	36 Propeller aperture	44 Line shaft section
2 Poop deck	11 Longitudinal deck girder	20 Stairway	29 Rudder post	37 Propeller	45 Line shaft bearing (plummer block)
3 Shelter deck	12 Transverse deck web	21 Hatch end pillar	30 Rudder	38 Stern bearing	46 Bearing foundation
4 Main deck	13 Deck longitudinal	22 After peak tank	31 Pintle	39 Stern tube nut	47 Shaft alley
5 Top of shaft alley	14 Pillars or stanchions	23 Swash plate	32 Gudgeon	40 Stern tube	48 Bottom floor
6 Tank top	15 Longitudinal bulkhead	24 Watertight bulkhead	33 Rudder stock	41 Tail shaft	49 Bottom longitudinal
7 Bottom plating	16 Cruiser stern	25 Top of after peak tank	34 Rudder stock trunk	42 Shaft stuffing box	50 Tank top longitudinal
8 Bulkhead	17 Vertical frame	26 Deep floor	35 Stuffing box	43 Coupling flanges	51 Heel of rudder post
9 Bulkhead stiffener	18 Shell longitudinals	27 Cement filling			

SOME STEERING GEARS

A *Steering arrangement in a big ship of the 17th century, when the rudder was controlled by a vertical lever called the whipstaff*
1 Rudder
2 Tiller
3 Whipstaff
4 Platform for the quartermaster
5 Hood for the quartermaster
6 Mizzenmast

B *Common steering gear in elevation and plan of small wooden sailing ship, 19th century*
1 Rudder
2 Tiller
3 Wheel stand
4 Tiller chain
5 Barrel or drum
6 Wheel

C *Mechanical screw steering gear in plan and elevation of big steel sailing ship, latter part of 19th century*
1 Rudder stock
2 Stuffing box on deck

3 Emergency tiller
4 Cross head
5 Coupling rods
6 Screw spindle-threaded right and left

7 Wheel
8 Wheel box with side seats
9 Wheel gratings
10 Log reel slung underneath wheel box

STABILIZERS

A *In the days of sail, ships were stabilized by the pressure of the wind on the sails*

B *Some very broad ships were built to reduce the rolling; this Russian royal yacht had a circular water line*

C *Today, many ships are equipped with stabilizers*

D *The stabilizers work as hydroplanes and can be turned through an arc of 50°*

E *The stabilizers work hydraulically on impulses from a gyroscope*

F *In harbor, or when the stabilizers are not in use, they can be housed in slots in the hull*

SOME COMMON FUNNELS

1 Furness Lines, London
2 Ellerman Lines, Ltd., London
3 Cie Générale Transatlantique, Paris
4 Blue Funnel Line, Liverpool
5 Broström Lines, Gothenburg
6 A. P. Möller, Copenhagen
7 Union Castle Mail S. S. Co., Ltd., London

8 Nederland N. V. Stoomvaart Maatschappij, Amsterdam
9 Lloyd Brasileiro, Rio de Janeiro
10 Nederlandsch-Amerikaansche Stoomvaart Maatschappij, Rotterdam
11 American Export Lines, Inc., New York
12 Moore-McCormack Lines, Inc., New York

13 Keystone Shipping Co., Philadelphia
14 Italia, Società Per Azioni di Navigazione, Genoa
15 East Asiatic Co., Ltd., Copenhagen
16 Canada Steam Ship Lines, Ltd., Montreal
17 Elder Dempster Lines Ltd., Liverpool
18 Rederi Transatlantic, Gothenburg

19 AS Westfal-Larsen & Co., Bergen
20 Scindia Steam Navigation Co., Ltd., Bombay
21 Osaka Shosen Kaisha, Osaka
22 Trafik AB Grängesberg—Oxelösund, Stockholm
23 N. V. Koninklijke Paketvaart Maatschappij, Amsterdam
24 Lloyd Triestino, Società Per Azioni di Navigazione, Trieste

25 Salén Lines, Stockholm
26 AS Knut Knutsen, Haugesund
27 Koninklijke Nederlandsche Stoomboot Maatschappij, Amsterdam
28 Hansa, Deutsche Dampschiffahrts-Gesellschaft, Bremen
29 Sigurd Herlofsen & Co., AS, Trondheim
30 Fred Olsen & Co., Oslo (motor ships)

31 Empresa Nacional, Madrid
32 A. F. Klavenes & Co., AS, Lysaker
33 Stockholms Rederi AB Svea, Stockholm
34 Hamburg—South American Line, Hamburg
35 Zim Israel Navigation Co., Ltd., Haifa
36 Finska Ångfartygs AB, Helsingfors

DECORATION

With most people illiterate, the name of a ship was often depicted by painted carvings on the stern, (for example A and B)

A The flower of the English hawthorn on the *Mayflower*, 1620 (from replica built in 1957)

B Stern of the Dutch pinnace *Dromedarus*, middle of the 17th century (from a model)

C Stern of the French ship *Le Soleil Royal*, built at Brest in 1669

D Head ornament of the three-masted fore-and aft schooner *Ellen* of Skärhamn, built at Thurö in 1908

E Name board of the Finnish barkentine *Ida*, wrecked on the west coast of Sweden in 1875

F Stern ornament of the three-masted fore-and aft schooner *Meta-Jan* of Skive, Denmark

DECORATION

A Sculptured lion's head on gun-port lid, perhaps intended to put heart in the crew and to frighten the enemy, the Swedish ship *Wasa*, 1628

B Figurehead of unknown vessel, from the middle of the 19th century

C Figurehead, from the 18th century

D Chinese junk with a painted eye on her bow, known as oculus decoration. "Suppose no eye no can see," the Chinese seamen says in his pidgin English. Such painted eyes may also be seen on fishing craft in the Mediterranean.

E Brigantine from the middle of the 19th century, with painted ports on her sides. This painting was originally intended to make the ship look like a man-of-war, but later it remained as decoration only.

F Dutch pinnace from the middle of the 17th century, with a painted waveline for a water line, to give an impression of speed. (Sketch from a model.)

LOAD LINES AND DRAFT MARKS

A *Ordinary and timber loadlines for steamships, starboard side shown*
1 Deck line
2 Loadline disc or Plimsoll mark. (The letters LR denote the classifying society, here Lloyd's Register)

3 Ordinary loadlines
The letters indicate:
TF=fresh water tropical loadline
SF=fresh water summer loadline
T=salt water tropical loadline
S=salt water summer loadline
W=salt water winter loadline

WNA=winter North Atlantic loadline
4 When loaded with timber (lumber) and with a deck cargo, the ship may be loaded somewhat deeper, and the timber loadlines are shown abaft the disc
The letters indicate:
LTF=fresh water tropical timber loadline

LSF=fresh water summer timber loadline
LT=salt water tropical timber loadline
LS=salt water summer timber loadline
LW=salt water winter timber loadline
LWNA=winter North Atlantic timber loadline

B *Loadlines of a sailing vessel are not so complicated*
1 Deck line
2 Loadline disc or Plimsoll mark (The horizontal bar across the disc gives summer loadline in salt water)
The letters indicate:
F=fresh water loadline

WNA=winter North Atlantic loadline
C *Draft marks*
The draft of ships is measured in feet and marked in six-inch-high Roman figures in such a way that 1 in the diagram indicates 20 feet, 2 indicates 20 feet 6 inches, and so on

A

B

DIFFERENT TYPES OF HULLS (BROKEN LINES INDICATE LIGHTER MATERIAL)

A

1 Flush-decked ship with two decks

2 Vessel with fo'c'sle and poop

3 Three-Island vessel (The reason for this name is the appearance of the ship when she is hull down on the horizon)

4 Vessel with extended bridge, fo'c'sle head, and poop

5 Spar-decked vessel (This type had lighter material above the main deck and, consequently, had to be given a lighter draft when loaded. Only passengers and lighter cargo could be carried under the spar deck)

6 Awning-decked vessel (It has a very light superstructure above the main deck and, so, has a high free board)

7 Well-decked vessel has the upper deckline broken, forming a well down to the main deck

8 Open shelter-decked vessel (This type has a tonnage opening (a) in the shelter deck which must not be permanently closed; the space above the main deck is not included in the gross tonnage)

9 Closed shelter-decked vessel has no tonnage opening; by a slight increase of scantlings the vessel may be loaded deeper

10 Raised quarter-deck vessel (This type was constructed to compensate for the loss of space caused by the propeller shaft tunnel)

11 Raised quarter-deck vessel with extended bridge

12 Turret vessel, no longer built

13 Trunk vessel

B *Different free boards*

I Full scantling ship

II Spar-decked ship

III Awning-decked ship

IV Shelter-decked ship

1 Main deck

2 Tween deck

3 Spar deck

4 Awning deck

5 Shelter deck

ANCHORS

A *Common anchor*
1 Anchor ring
2 Stock
3 Hoops of the anchor
   stock
4 Shank
5 Crown
6 Arm
7 Fluke
8 Pea or bill

B *Part of tree trunk with branches, used as an anchor*

C *Anchor, made from tree branches and stone*

D *Roman anchor of Caligula from Lake Nemi*

E *Viking anchor from the Oseberg ship*

ANCHORS AND ANCHOR GEAR

F Grapnel
G Iron-stocked anchor
H Trotman's anchor
I Inglefield's anchor
J Mushroom anchor
K Hall's anchor

L Cathead with anchor
   gear
1 Anchor
2 Cable
3 Shackle
4 Cathead
5 Releasing gear
6 Cathead stopper

M Arrangement for fish-
   ing an anchor
1 Pendant with fish
   tackle
2 Cathead
3 Chain cable

N Chain cable
1 Shackle
2 Stud link
3 Swivel

O Patent link
P, Q Hawser bends

WINDLASS AND CAPSTAN

A *Windlass*
1 Pawl bitt
2 Windlass bitts
3 Cheeks of windlass
   bitts
4 Standard knees
5 Warping heads
6 Windlass barrel with
   whelps

7 Strongback
8 Crosshead
9 Purchase rod
10 Pawl
11 Pawl rim
12 Purchase rims

B *Capstan*
1 Head
2 Bar holes
3 Barrel
4 Whelps

C *Old windlass*
1 Windlass bitt
2 Cheek of windlass
   bitts
3 Bolts
4 Windlass barrel
5 Bar holes

D *Method of heaving an-
   chor with a messenger*
1 Cable
2 Cathead
3 Nippers
4 Messenger (an endless
   rope)
5 Capstan
6 Capstan bars

WINDLASSES AND CAPSTANS

A *Patent steam windlass*
1 Levers, hand-power levers
2 Crosshead
3 Warping heads
4 Side bitts
5 Bearing caps
6 Screwbrake nuts
7 Wildcats (Gypsies)
8 Windlass barrel or drum
9 Main cone driving wheels
10 Crosshead bracket
11 Cable relievers
12 Chain pipes
13 Bandbrakes
14 Cylinders
15 Steampipe flange
16 Valve casings
17 Bedplate

B *Electric windlass*
1 Bedplate
2 Side bitts
3 Wildcats (Gypsies)
4 Toothwheels
5 Operating clutches
6 Operating handles
7 Brakes
8 Brake handles
9 Pinion shafts
10 Warping heads
11 Gear coupling
12 Worm gears
13 Driving shafts
14 Electric motors

C *Capstan*
1 Drumhead
2 Capstan-bar holes
3 Barrel
4 Whelps
5 Whelp chocks
6 Pawls
7 Pawl rim
8 Capstan partners
9 Deck planking

WINCHES

A *Steam winch*
1 Warping heads or gypsy heads
2 Winch drum
3 Main cogwheel
4 Reversing link
5 Pinion shaft cogwheel
6 Clutch lever
7 Cylinders
8 Slide-valve box

9 Steam exhaust pipe
10 Inlet steampipe
11 Tie rod, stay
12 Throttle valve
13 Reversing lever
14 Drum shaft bearing
15 Connecting rod
16 Bedplate

17 Piston rod and cross-head
18 Crank pin
19 Combined gear- and flywheel
20 Strap-brake pedal
21 Weigh shaft

B *15/5 ton automatic or constant-tension mooring winch*
1 Winch drum
2 Warping head
3 Drum shaft
4 Gear casing
5 Gear lever, 5 or 15 tons
6 Electric coupling box
7 Electric driving motor
8 Lamina brake

9 Strap-brake tightening screw
10 Strap-brake
11 Warping head coupling handle
12 Foundation

C *Worm-geared vertical cargo winch*
1 Winch drum
2 Warping head
3 Worm-gear house
4 Gear lever, 2 or 5 tons
5 Electric coupling box
6 Electric motor (vertical shaft)
7 Lamina brake
8 Bedplate
9 Foundation

BELLS, HOURGLASS, AND WHISTLES

A A little bell placed aft, on which the helmsman struck the time, and which was repeated by the lookout at the main bell

B A bell hanging in a belfry, Nelson's *Victory*

C Hourglass, measuring half an hour. Each glass on board accounts for half an hour, and is sounded by one stroke of the bell; each watch of four hours is divided into eight glasses, corresponding to eight bells. The six watches are: the 1st watch 20—24, the 2nd watch (middle watch) 00—04, the day watch (morning watch) 04—08, the forenoon watch 08—12, the noon watch 12—16, and the afternoon watch 16—20. Three bells thus mean that the time is 01.30, 05.30, 09.30, 13.30, 17.30, or 21.30. Eight bells mean that a watch is over. The number of glasses is struck on the bell as a series of double strokes. For instance, 15.30 (seven glasses):

++ ++ ++ +
Eight bells mean a watch is over

D Boatswain's call

E Fog horn made from a bullock's horn

F Fog horn of copper

G Sirens and whistles

1 Siren

2 Bell whistle

3 Chime whistle

4 Organ pipe whistle

ACCOMMODATIONS

Up to the middle of the 17th century the crew had no special accommodations but had to sleep on the bare deck or find a place for themselves. Meals were eaten on deck without tables or chairs.

A *Early 19th century* When hammocks were used in the navy they were slung from the deck-head beams; they were stowed in the top-gallant bulwark for protection against musket fire when not in use
1 Hammocks slung under deck beams
2 Hammocks stowed in bulwark
3 Mess table slung from overhead beam
4 Muzzle-loading gun with wooden carriage

B *Cabin accommodations on board a Swedish barkentine, built in Gävle, 1878*
1 Mizzenmast
2 Mess room
3 Mate's room
4 Second mate's and steward's room
5 Pantry
6 Cabin
7 Captain's bedroom
8 Alleyway

9 Sail locker and deck stores
10 Provisions
11 Entrance from deck
12 Steering compass

C *Accommodation for 12 seamen in fo'c'sle on board a British three-masted iron bark of 900 tons, built in Glasgow, 1879*
1 Upper and lower bunks
2 Hawse pipes

3 Bowsprit
4 Cable compressors
5 Fore peak hatch
6 Windlass
7 Hatch to chain locker
8 Crew's lavatory with light house above
9 Fore hatch

D *Modern staterooms*
1 Officer's room
2 Seaman's room
3 Berth
4 Sofa
5 Table
6 Armchair
7 Desk
8 Chair
9 Washroom
10 Wardrobe
11 Washstand

GALLEY

A *Open sheet-iron fireplace, on the deck of a coaster in the Indian Ocean*

B *Brick fireplace on board the Swedish ship Wasa, 1628. There was no chimney and the smoke had to find its way out wherever it could.*

C *Ship's galley, according to Chapman, 1768*
1 Pea-soup kettle
2 Brick fireplace
3 Galley stacks

D *Big galley stove, from the beginning of the 20th century*

E *Modern ship's galley*
1 Electric stove
2 Roaster
3 Dumbwaiter
4 Garbage chute
5 Steamer, steam kettles
6 Electric control panel
7 Refrigerator
8 Mixer
9 Sink
10 Oven

PUMPS

A *Single-stage centrifugal pump*
1 Pump shaft drive
2 Ball bearing
3 Oil-filled bearing box
4 Gland sealing
5 Pump casing
6 Discharge flange
7 Impeller
8 Suction flange
9 Mounting flange

B *Duplex-type, direct-acting pump*
1 Steam inlet
2 Cylinder lubricator
3 Slide-valve box
4 Steam cylinder
5 Slide-valve rod
6 Gland sealing
7 Drain and air cocks
8 Piston rod
9 Rocker arm
10 Crosshead connection
11 Column
12 Discharge flange
13 Gland sealing
14 Suction and discharge valve box
15 Suction flange
16 Pump cylinder

C *Old-type bilge pump, once common in small craft in the Baltic area. It was constructed from a piece of leather, which formed a bag, and gave good service.*

D *The standard bilge pump in small wooden sailing vessels. It was made from a straight tree trunk, bored through the heart.*
1 Trunk of pump
2 Pump bucket
3 Pump brake, handle

E *Windmill pump with four sails, mounted on a turntable on top of a bipod erection. The windmill pump always had rigging. The three-masted fore-and-aft schooner, Eufrosine of Reval, had a windmill pump forward of the foremast.*
1 Sails as seen from the side
2 Crankshaft
3 Turntable
4 Arm with braces, for setting the mill to the wind
5 The pump deck seating
6 Front view of windmill, showing two sails furled and two set
7 Three-masted fore-and-aft schooner with a windmill pump

A

B

C

A

B

C

D1

2

3

4

5

6

LANTERNS

A Swedish poop lantern from the 18th century

B Lantern with horn windows from the 18th century

C Riding light with a round wick lamp and Fresnel lens (A.J. Fresnel, French physicist, 1788-1827)

D Development of the poop lantern
1 1514, Great Harry
2 Middle of the 16th century, Sir Francis Drake's Golden Hind

3 The 17th century, Dutch poop lantern
4 The 17th century, English poop lantern, Prince Royal

5 The 18th century, poop lantern of a big French ship, built at Brest in 1756
6 The 18th century, Swedish poop lantern (same as A)

A ·—	N —·	1 ·————
B —···	O ———	2 ··———
C —·—·	P ·——·	3 ···——
D —··	Q ——·—	4 ····—
E ·	R ·—·	5 ·····
F ··—·	S ···	6 —····
G ——·	T —	7 ——···
H ····	U ··—	8 ———··
I ··	V ···—	9 ————·
J ·———	W ·——	0 —————
K —·—	X —··—	
L ·—··	Y —·——	
M ——	Z ——··	

LANTERNS AND SIDELIGHTS

A *Sidelight for kerosene, paraffin oil, from the beginning of the 20th century*

B *Starboard side light house on board big sailing ship, the 19th and 20th centuries*

C *Morse lamp for merchant ship, all around illumination*

D *Day Morse lamp for a man-of-war*

E *Morse code (named after its inventor, S.F.B. Morse, 1791—1872)*

F *Electric light cluster for illumination of gangways, holds, etc.*

G *Searchlight*

H *Arcs of lights*

1 Masthead light (fore steaming light), from right ahead over an arc of 112½° to each side (total arc 225°)

2 Range light (after steaming light), from right ahead over an arc of 112½° to each side (total arc 225°)

3 Stern light (overtaking light), from right astern over an arc of 67½° to each side (total arc 135°)

4 Starboard side light, from right ahead over an arc of 112½° to starboard

5 Port side light, from right ahead over an arc of 112½° to port

J *Lights of different ships, under way at night, seen from straight ahead*

1 Sailing vessel

2 Power-driven vessel with a length of less than 150 ft.

3 Power-driven vessel with range light (after steaming light); this light is to be carried by vessels over 150 ft. in length. The figure may also indicate a tug with two masthead lights (fore steaming lights), that is, with a tow not exceeding 600 ft.

4 A tug with three masthead lights (fore steaming lights), length of tow over 600 ft., may also indicate a tug with two masthead lights (fore steaming lights), one range light (after steaming light); the tow must then not exceed 600 ft.

5 Power-driven pilot vessel; in addition, a white flare is burnt at intervals not exceeding 10 minutes

6 Steam trawler at night. The upper masthead light (steaming light) (I) is showing green, white, and red lights See lower sketch

7 Vessel not under command, but steaming

8 Cable-laying vessel under way

SOME TYPES OF LIFEBOAT DAVITS

A *Medieval ship towing her barge*

B *Auxiliary coaster with her boat slung from short davits across her transom stern*

C *Radical davit*
1 Davit
2 Boat fall
3 Leading block
4 Staghorn bollard
5 Gripes
6 Boat chocks
7 Hinged chocks on the outboard side

D *Quadrant davit*
1 Crank for turning out davit
2 Gripes holding boat steady
3 Toothed quadrant

E *Gravity davit*
1 Cradle mounted on rollers
2 Trackway
3 Boat fall
4 Winch for hoisting and lowering boat

LIFEBOATS

The 1948 Convention for Safety of Life at Sea states that all lifeboats must be open boats with rigid sides having internal buoyancy only, and they are now frequently being built of metal or plastic. The buoyancy of metal boats should be allotted so as to give the same buoyancy as in wooden boats.

Internal buoyancy should consist of tanks having at least 10 % of the total space in a wooden boat. Formerly, when external buoyancy and collapsible sides were allowed, the lifeboats were divided into different classes as follows:

A *Lifeboat class I a*
Open boat with rigid sides and internal buoyancy tanks

B *Lifeboat class I b*
Open boat with rigid sides and both internal buoyancy tanks and external buoyancy

C *Lifeboat class II*
Open or decked boat with both internal and external buoyancy and with collapsible sides. Only for passenger vessels needing many boats

A—C
1 Buoyancy tank
2 External buoyancy (cork or plastic)

D *Lifeboat class III*
Open boat with rigid sides, but without any buoyancy

E *Mills release apparatus*
1 Block
2 Releasing handle
3 Hook holding the block until the handle is pulled
4 Weight keeping the hook in place

F *Life buoy*
1 Life line
2 Battery operated self-igniting buoyant light

G *Carley life float*

H *Modern inflatable life raft; canopy attached, filled by CO_2 bottle*
1 Buoyancy tube
2 Life line
3 Canopy
4 Drain tube
5 Light

The SANTA MARIA *is
shown once again to
introduce the chapter
on spars and rigging.
There is not much
rigging left on modern
ships, therefore most
of this chapter will deal
with times gone by.*

SPARS AND RIGGING

BY SAM SVENSSON

Exactly when and where primitive man first rigged a mast and sail to his simple boat remains a mystery. But quite early, he must have noticed that if he stood up in his craft, he would drift in the direction in which the wind was blowing. If he wanted to go in this direction, he might very well have speeded up his journey by holding up a cloak or animal hide to catch the wind. The time that elapsed between this first step and the introduction of the first real mast was certainly extremely long. And for many thousands of years a single mast and a simple square sail were the limit of the ancient sailor's ability to rig a boat.

Far along through the ages, from the Old Empire in Egypt and well into the European Middle Ages, the single mast remained the only rig. One break in the monotony comes in the Roman era, when the Roman sailing ship had a bowsprit, sometimes seen as a greatly inclined foremast.

In Mediterranean lands, where the rowing galley played an important role, the mast and sail evolved somewhat differently than in Western Europe, where the single mast and square sail were prevalent up to the beginning of the 15th century. The standing rigging was very simple. Smaller ships at times had none, as in the rudimentary sailing boats of the early Scandinavian fishermen.

The running gear also was very simple. The halliard hoisting the sail was led aft and acted as a backstay, thus also serving to strengthen the mast when sailing. In the early Middle Ages bowlines were added to the sail and led forward to a spar, called the bowsprit, which was rigged out over the stem.

The shrouds were set up with deadeyes and lanyards, and the rigging was rattled down, forming rope ladders to facilitate going aloft. The Northern ship was also given a fighting top at the masthead. This top is actually very old. In fact, our oldest reproduction of the fighting top is to be found on an Egyptian relief from about 1200 B.C. The oldest top mentioned in Scandinavia is in the saga of Haakon Hardabred, 1159, contained in *Snorres Konungasagor.*

Sometime during the first half of the 15th century larger ships were built with two or three masts. In northwest Europe evolution quickly culminated in three masts. The mainmast kept its location in the middle of the ship, and from the beginning the new masts were stepped in the fore- and aftercastles. As improvements were made, it was most likely that flags or banners were first flown there, a common practice during the Crusades, and that it was just as easy to hoist a small sail on this same flag-pole. One could even go so far as to say that every square sail, except the first, of course, was preceded by a flag on a pole. Thus, big ships unfurled a banner aloft on a staff in the fighting top, and toward the end of the 15th century they appeared with a small sail on the same staff. From the beginning this small sail was handled by the men in the top, and it was from this that the name topsail was derived. The Dutch, Germans, and Scandinavians used a similar term; to them the sail was known as the "märssegel." The main topsail was soon followed by a second sail on the foremast. Both were small at first, but they continually increased in size as they came to be used more and more. The clews were sheeted to the yardarms below, and, with braces and clewlines leading down to the deck, the sail became more functional. As it could be set flatter, it could be used when sailing on the wind.

The triangular lateen sail, in general use in galleys and fishing boats of the Mediterranean, was eventually used as the mizzen in big ships all along the European coast. Its use had spread all the way to the Baltic Sea by the end of the Middle Ages. There, it gradually supplanted the older square sail as the mizzen. In the 250 years that followed, the lateen mizzen continued to be used in all larger ships.

The bowsprit had originally served only to lead the bowlines. By the end of the Middle Ages, however, a square sail had been rigged under the bowsprit. This sail was called a blind in Medieval English, as it wholly blocked the view ahead. It was, perhaps, the blind that prompted the need for a lookout aloft. Later, it became known as the spritsail.

By the last quarter of the 15th century larger ships began to have as many as four masts. The two aftermost masts generally had lateen sails only, but the main mizzenmast could carry a triangular topsail on a topmast as well. The smaller mizzen, known as the bonaventure mizzen, usually reached abaft the ship where it was sheeted to a spar rigged out over the stern.

The topsail continued to grow in size, and around the middle of the 16th century larger ships began to carry a third square sail, the topgallant sail, on the fore- and mainmasts. Until this time, however, the topmasts had been fixed extensions of the masts themselves and could not be rigged down. But around the 1570's, topmasts began to be stepped, to be fidded as the term was, so they could be rigged up or taken down depending on circumstances. This innovation, credited to the Dutch, was found to be very practical and was soon adopted for general use. Consequently, the fidded topmasts grew larger in relation to the lower masts; the topsail grew deeper, and the lower sail shallower.

Around 1620 it was common to equip the third mast with a square topsail. At the same time, the bonaventure mizzenmast was discarded. This marked the creation of the three-masted ship, with square sails on each mast. These early ships always had one yard less on the mizzenmast than on the fore- and mainmasts.

It was not until the latter half of the 18th century that rigging had evolved to the point where each mast had the same number of yards. This was the time when the term full-rigged ship became universal. The full-rigged ship usually referred to a merchant vessel, while sailing warships with such a rig were referred to by their rating: ship of the line, frigate, or sloop. The ships of the early 17th century were built with low heads and high sterns.

This design made them very hard to steer when the wind was abaft the beam, and the need for more headsail was keenly felt. To remedy the problem all larger ships of the 19th century were rigged with a spritsail topsail on a small mast at the end of the bowsprit. This sail was very impractical, though it was found to be very necessary, and it remained in use for over a hundred years before it was replaced with more practical and effective staysails.

Staysails had been used quite early in small craft, but not in the big ships. By the 1670's, however, the larger ships began carrying staysails, first between the masts and later over the bowsprit. This fore topmast staysail over the bowsprit was difficult to set because of the complicated rigging of the spritsail and sprit topsail. This was also the case with the staysails between the masts, because of the braces and bowlines leading to the stays. The staysails won out over the others, though, and in the beginning of the 18th century the spritsail topmast was discarded and the running gear was gradually changed to make more room for the staysails of the mainmast. This development continued through the entire 18th century, and by the end of the century larger ships carried a staysail on every possible stay.

When the spritsail topmast was discarded in the first decade of the 18th century, a new spar, the jib boom, was rigged out on the bowsprit. A new staysail, called the jib, was placed over the fore topmast staysail. After the middle of the same century the lateen mizzen's long yard was exchanged for a gaff. This change occurred earlier in the smaller vessels than in the big ones.

During the Napoleonic wars, at the end of the century, other changes began to take place in the rigging. The mizzen was enlarged and sheeted to a boom extending over the stern. Under the bowsprit a new spar, called the martingale or dolphin striker, was inserted to improve the staying of the jib boom. This all developed into a new spar and staysail, the flying jib boom and flying jib, which were rigged outside the jib. A fourth yard above the topgallant yard, called the royal yard, now became

more and more common on larger ships. Men-of-war always set it flying, while merchant ships set it as a standing sail carried on the upper part of the long topgallant mast. Only on hard winter trips was it rigged down. But this, of course, was true of all unnecessary rigging in prolonged bad weather.

The 19th century's mechanical revolution gradually began to influence the rigging of sailing ships. At first, it was merely a replacement on masts and yards of rope fittings, strops, and so on, with forged iron bands. Then the rope trusses of the lower yards were replaced with iron trusses, called patent trusses. Wherever possible, the heavier running rigging was replaced with chain, first the topsail ties and sheets and then the topgallant ties and sheets, and then just about anywhere chain could be used to advantage. By the middle of the 19th century British ships began to have the standing rigging replaced with wire. The rigging had previously been made of tarred hemp rope, but wire was cheaper and stronger and more durable. It had less surface exposed to the wind, and as the early attempts to build iron vessels were crowned with success, wire rigging was used more and more on larger ships, especially on steamships, which always had rigging and sails by the 19th century.

The huge topsails on larger sailing ships were extremely hard to handle during storms, when they had to be reefed. The American captain, Robert Forbes, devised a rig with double topsails in 1841. In 1854, another American sea captain, named Howes, improved this rig, and it became common in big ships. Twenty years later, in 1874, the largest ships were also rigged with double topgallant yards, as well as double topsail yards.

By this time the use of wire for standing rigging and of chain for sheets and halliards was entirely accepted. Standing rigging now featured turnbuckles instead of deadeyes and lanyards, the system used ever since the early Middle Ages. Strong but stiff tarred hemp was replaced with Manila rope for running gear. Manila rope was softer and easier to work and just as strong, though

not as durable as the hemp used formerly. Block sheaves were furnished with roller bearings, which also served to lighten the work on board ship. In fact, so much was done to ease the work on deck and aloft that the vessels could now be sailed with fewer hands, and larger ships could be sailed with the same crew as had been required for a smaller ship twenty years earlier. Sail handling became more mechanized in the large ships. In the 1890's, the Scottish sea captain, J.C.B. Jarvis, devised a geared mechanical winch that allowed a couple of men to brace the yards in the largest ships in rough weather. This was, of course, a big help. In the last of the big ships the topsail and topgallant halliards of chain were replaced with wire regulated by a hand-operated drum winch. Equipped with a conical drum, the winch considerably eased the effort of raising the yard.

All these innovations were part of that universal sequence of events that provided labor-saving devices in many areas of trade. For the sailing ship, these innovations had to be adapted to the special needs of the sea. They were needed to enable the sailing ship, with only the wind for power, to face up to the competition now provided by the coal- and oil-burning ships of the new age. It was obviously not a successful struggle, and the new means of propulsion became a prime factor in the disappearance of the sailing ship from all the seas of the world.

SPARS OF A FOUR-MASTED BARK

1 Spike bowsprit
2 Fore lower mast
3 Fore yard
4 Fore top
5 Fore lower topsail yard
6 Fore topmast
7 Fore upper topsail yard, hoisted
8 Lifts
9 Fore topmast crosstree

10 Fore lower topgallant yard
11 Fore topgallant mast
12 Fore upper topgallant yard, hoisted
13 Fore royal mast in one with topgallant mast
14 Fore royal yard, hoisted
15 Fore royal pole
16 Main lower mast
17 Mainyard

18 Main top
19 Main lower topsail yard
20 Main topmast
21 Main upper topsail yard, hoisted
22 Main topmast crosstree
23 Main lower topgallant yard
24 Main topgallant mast
25 Main upper topgallant yard, hoisted

26 Main royal mast
27 Main royal yard, hoisted
28 Main royal pole
29 Mizzen lower mast
30 Crossjack yard
31 Mizzen top
32 Mizzen lower topsail yard
33 Mizzen topmast

34 Mizzen upper topsail yard, hoisted
35 Mizzen topmast crosstree
36 Mizzen lower topgallant yard
37 Mizzen topgallant mast
38 Mizzen upper topgallant yard, hoisted
39 Mizzen royal mast
40 Mizzen royal yard, hoisted

41 Mizzen pole
42 Jigger lower mast
43 Jigger top
44 Jigger topmast
45 Jigger pole
46 Spanker boom
47 Lower spanker gaff
48 Upper spanker gaff
49 Upper topsail halliard
50 Upper topgallant halliard
51 Royal halliard

MASTS OF DIFFERENT SHIPS

A *Three-masted full-rigged ship*
1 Foremast
2 Mainmast
3 Mizzenmast

B *Four-masted full-rigged ship*
1 Foremast
2 Mainmast
3 Mizzenmast
4 Jiggermast

C *Five-masted full-rigged ship*
1 Foremast
2 Mainmast
3 Middlemast
4 Mizzenmast
5 Jiggermast

D *Three-masted bark*
1 Foremast
2 Mainmast
3 Mizzenmast

E *Four-masted bark*
1 Foremast
2 Mainmast
3 Mizzenmast
4 Jiggermast

F *Five-masted bark*
1 Foremast
2 Mainmast
3 Middlemast
4 Mizzenmast
5 Jiggermast

G *Brig*
1 Foremast
2 Mainmast

H *Brigantine*
1 Foremast
2 Mainmast

I *Three-masted barkentine*
1 Foremast
2 Mainmast
3 Mizzenmast

J *Six-masted barkentine*
1 Foremast
2 Mainmast
3 Mizzenmast
4 Jiggermast
5 Driver mast
6 Spanker mast

K *Ketch*
1 Mainmast
2 Mizzenmast

L *Two-masted fore-and-aft schooner*
1 Foremast
2 Mainmast

M *Three-masted fore-and-aft schooner*
1 Foremast
2 Mainmast
3 Mizzenmast

N *Four-masted fore-and-aft schooner*
1 Foremast
2 Mainmast
3 Mizzenmast
4 Spanker mast

O *Six-masted fore-and-aft schooner*
1 Foremast
2 Mainmast
3 Mizzenmast
4 Jiggermast
5 Driver mast
6 Spanker mast

P *Five-masted fore-and-aft schooner*
1 Foremast
2 Mainmast
3 Mizzenmast
4 Jiggermast
5 Spanker mast

Q *Seven-masted fore-and-aft schooner*
1 Foremast
2 Mainmast
3 Mizzenmast
4 Jiggermast
5 Driver mast
6 Pusher mast
7 Spanker mast

Regarding the names of masts of a seven-masted schooner, see also page 132

MASTS AND SPARS IN DIFFERENT SHIPS

A *Yawl*
B *Sloop, about 1900*
C *Ketch, end of the 19th century*
D *Topsail schooner*
E *Barkentine*
F *Three-masted fore-and-aft schooner*
G *American five-masted fore-and-aft schooner*

1	Mast coat
2	Truck
3	Foremast
4	Mainmast
5	Snow mast
8	Mizzenmast
9	Laeisz mast
10	Lower mast
11	Fore-and-aft-rigged topmast
12	Square-rigged topmast

13	Topgallant mast
14	Royal mast
15	Skysail mast
16	Moonsail mast
17	Fore yard
18	Main yard
19	Crossjack yard
20	Topsail yard for single topsail
21	Lower topsail yard
22	Upper topsail yard
23	Topgallant yard for single topgallant sail

24	Lower topgallant yard
25	Upper topgallant yard
26	Royal yard
27	Skysail yard
28	Moonsail yard
29	Masthead and housing of topmast
30	Jiggermast
31	Spankermast
32	Flagpole
33	Laeisz yard
34	Jigger yard

The terminology for masts varies in different languages. Numbers 6 and 7, missing in list above, refer to Teutonic languages only.

H

I

J

K

H *Snow with single top-sails*

I *Three-masted bark with double topsails*

J *Four-masted bark with short topgallant masts abaft the top-masts*

K *Four-masted bark with royals and double topgallant sails, skysails on the main and the mizzen*

L *Three-masted, full-rigged ship, American clipper, about 1850, with skysails and a main moonsail*

M *Ship, about 1700*

N *Five-masted full-rigged ship (Preussen, the only ship of this rig ever built)*

L

M

N

1 Mast coat	12 Square-rigged topmast	21 Lower topsail yard	28 Moonsail yard
2 Truck	13 Topgallant mast	22 Upper topsail yard	29 Masthead and housing
3 Foremast	14 Royal mast	23 Topgallant yard for	of topmast
4 Mainmast	15 Skysail mast	single topgallant sail	30 Jiggermast
5 Snow mast	16 Moonsail mast	24 Lower topgallant yard	31 Spankermast
8 Mizzenmast	17 Fore yard	25 Upper topgallant yard	32 Flagpole
9 Laeisz mast	18 Main yard	26 Royal yard	33 Laeisz yard
10 Lower mast	19 Crossjack yard	27 Skysail yard	34 Jigger yard
11 Fore-and-aft-rigged	20 Topsail yard for single		
topmast	topsail		

The terminology for masts varies in different languages. Numbers 6 and 7, missing in list above, refer to Teutonic languages only.

MASTS AND TOPS

A *Early medieval top*
B *Medieval top*
C *Medieval top*

D *Top, about 1550*
I *Top from the end of the 17th century*
J *Mast from the end of the 17th century (from an old book on ship building)*

1 Mast step in keelson
2 Lower mast
3 Cheeks
4 Trestletrees supporting rigging and topmast

5 Lower cap
6 Topmast
7 Topmast crosstree
8 Topmast cap
9 Topgallant mast

10 Topgallant crosstree
11 Topgallant cap
12 Flagpole
13 Truck

A

B

STANDING RIGGING OF A FOUR-MASTED BARK

A *Jigger mast* (identical
  with mizzenmast of a
  three-masted bark)
1 Jigger lower mast
2 Jigger topmast
3 Jigger topgallant mast
4 Jigger topgallant stay

5 Jigger topmast stay
6 Jigger topmast rigging
  or shrouds
7 Jigger stay
8 Jigger rigging or
  jigger shrouds

B *Foremast* (identical with
  mainmast and mizzen-
  mast except in the lead
  of the stays)
1 Fore lower mast
2 Fore topmast
3 Fore topgallant mast
4 Fore royal mast
5 Fore royal stay

6 Fore topgallant stay
7 Outer jib stay
8 Inner jib stay
9 Fore topmast stay
10 Fore stay
11 Fore rigging or shrouds
12 Fore cap backstays

13 Fore topmast backstays
14 Fore topmast rigging
  or shrouds
15 Fore topmast cap
  backstay
16 Fore topgallant
  backstays
17 Fore royal backstay
18 Fore topgallant rigging
  or shrouds

19 Main royal stay
20 Main topgallant stay
21 Main topmast stay
22 Main stay
23 Bob stay
24 Outer bob stay

A

I

II

B

C

STAYS AND SHROUDS

A *Square-rigged foremast of a big modern sailing ship as seen from aft, with the sails furled on the port side (I) and set on the starboard side (II)*

1 Lower rigging or shrouds
2 Cap backstay
3 Futtock rigging, futtock shrouds
4 Royal back stay
5 Topgallant backstay(s)
6 Topmast cap backstay
7 Topmast backstay(s)
8 Topmast rigging, topmast shrouds
9 Topmast futtock rigging
10 Topgallant rigging, topgallant shrouds

B *This picture of a top, seen from the side, shows how shrouds and stays are fastened to the mast*

C *The same top as B, here seen from ahead*

DIFFERENT PARRELS

A *Parrel with cleats on a wooden yard*
1 Topmast
2 Yard
3 Wooden cleats
4 Half-iron hoop served with leather

5 Pins forming hinges to open the parrel
6 Iron band to take the tie
7 Iron straps and bolts securing parrel to yard

B *Tub parrel for iron yard*
1 Topmast
2 Yard
3 Tub divided in halves
4 Iron binding for same
5 Gooseneck bolt

6 Iron bands to take parrel and tie
7 Yoke for the parrel
8 Yoke for the tie
9 Eye bolt for quarter-block

C *Parrel, sliding on T-bar in a big ship*
1 Topmast
2 Topsail yard
3 T-bar
4 Slide

5 Two-way coupling
6 Tie
7 Connecting chain keeping slide in place
8 Eye bolts for quarter-blocks

A

B

TOP AND CROSSTREES IN A BIG MODERN SAILING SHIP

A *Details around the top*

1 Topmast, built in one with lower mast
2 Lower topsail yard with its truss
3 Lower topsail yard tie
4 Lower cap backstays
5 Quarter block for upper topsail sheet and topsail clewline

6 Topmast rigging, ratlines not shown
7 Futtock shrouds
8 Top
9 Fairleader
10 Running gear rove through fairleader
11 Lower yard with its truss
12 Lower yard tie
13 Lower stay, doubled
14 Lower rigging, ratlines not shown

15 Pendants for braces from mast ahead, leading to brace winch
16 Quarterblock for top-sail sheet and the course clewgarnet
17 Buntline with its leading blocks

B *Details around the topgallant crosstrees*

1 Topmast
2 Topgallant mast
3 Topmast head
4 Topgallant crosstrees
5 Spreader of topgallant backstays
6 Topmast cap
7 Lower topgallant yard
8 Lower topgallant truss
9 Lower topgallant tie

10 Upper topsail yard
11 Upper topsail parrel, slide running on a T-bar
12 Topsail halliard, wire tackle leading to winch on deck
13 Leading block for top-sail brace from mast ahead
14 Topmast backstays
15 Topmast cap backstay

16 Topgallant futtock shrouds
17 Topmast stay
18 Topgallant rigging
19 Spreader lift
20 Quarterblock for lower topgallant clewline and upper topgallant sheet
21 Quarterblock for top-sail downhaul and lower topgallant sheet

LOWER PART OF RIGGING, PORT SIDE

1 Shrouds, lower ends of which are served with spun yarn
2 Upper deadeye
3 Deadeye turned in cutter-stay fashion
4 Lower deadeye in iron strap
5 Chain plate
6 Lanyard, standing part with wall knot
7 Wall knot
8 Double wall knot
9 Hauling end of lanyard hitched
10 Surplus end of lanyard made up
11 Setting up a shroud by luff upon luff
12 Luff clapped on lanyard up and down
13 Selvagee on shroud parceled for protection
14 Selvagee strapped on lanyard with a toggle
15 Double Blackwall hitch
16 Lower block of burton from masthead
17 Standing end of lanyard passed around neck of deadeye
18 Ratlines in rigging
19 Seizing of ratline to shroud
20 Wooden batten secured to shroud with seizing wire

SEIZINGS AND RIGGING SCREWS

A Three stages of making
   an old-fashioned round
   seizing; formerly used
   on hemp shrouds

B 1 Shroud or backstay
      of wire served over
      with spun yarn
   2 Rigging seizings of
      galvanized wire

3 Solid heart thimble
   with a hole for the
   sheer pole
4 Upper end of rigging
   screw

C 1 Lower ends of four
      port side shrouds
   2 Rigging seizings
   3 Sheer pole

4 Rigging screws or
   turnbuckles
5 Upper ends of chain
   plates

BOWSPRIT OF A FRIGATE, 1890

1 Bowsprit
2 Tenon for bowsprit cap
3 Bowsprit cap
4 Bowsprit bees
5 Jib boom
6 Heel of flying jib boom
7 Martingale boom or dolphin striker
8 Whisker
9 Inner and outer bobstays
10 Bowsprit shrouds
11 Forestay
12 Preventer forestay
13 Fore topmast stay
14 Fore topmast preventer stay
15 Jib stay
16 Jib outhaul
17 Jib boom guy
18 Flying jib boom guy
19 Martingale stay
20 Backropes or martingale guys
21 Flying jib stay
22 Fore topgallant stay
23 Fore royal stay
24 Jib boom horse, footrope
25 Gaskets
26 Fore topsail bowline
27 Whisker lift
28 Fore topmast staysail tack
29 Jib boom gammoning
30 Jib boom heel stay
31 Lanyards for stays
32 Iron fitting for whiskers

THE BOWSPRIT DURING THREE CENTURIES

A *The bowsprit and its rigging at the end of the 16th century*
1 Foremast
2 Bowsprit
3 Spritsail yard
4 Jackstaff
5 Foreyard
6 Foresail with bonnet
7 Fore topsail
8 Spritsail
9 Gammoning
10 Forestay lanyard
11 Fore topmast stay
12 Fore topgallant stay
13 Fore sheet
14 Fore tack
15 Spritsail sheet
16 Spritsail clewline
17 Spritsail braces
18 Spritsail lifts
19 Fore topsail bowline
20 Fore topgallant bowline

B *Bowsprit with spritsail topmast and rigging, from the 17th century*
1 Foremast
2 Bowsprit
3 Spritsail yard
4 Spritsail topmast
5 Spritsail topsail yard
6 Fore rigging
7 Gammoning
8 Forestay
9 Fore topmast stay
10 Fore topgallant stay
11 Spritsail topmast backstay
12 Fore sheet
13 Fore tack
14 Fore clewgarnet
15 Fore bowline
16 Spritsail sheet
17 Spritsail clewline
18 Spritsail braces
19 Fore topsail bowline
20 Fore topgallant bowline
21 Spritsail topsail sheet
22 Spritsail topsail clewline
23 Spritsail topsail braces
24 Spritsail topsail lift

C *Bowsprit with jib boom and rigging, end of the 18th century*
1 Bowsprit
2 Jib boom
3 Flying jib boom
4 Spritsail yard
5 Foreyard
6 Studdingsail boom
7 Fore tack bumpkin
8 Bobstay
9 Forestay
10 Fore topmast stay
11 Jibstay
12 Fore topgallant stay
13 Flying jibstay
14 Royal stay
15 Jib boom guy
16 Flying jib boom guy
17 Spritsail braces
18 Fore topmast staysail downhaul
19 Weather side jib sheet
20 Weather side flying jib sheet

BOWSPRIT OF THE SHIP, PRINCE OSCAR, BUILT IN 1864

1 Shark's tail	10 Outer jib downhaul	19 Bowsprit cap	25 Fore topmast staysail
2 Fore royal stay	11 Outer jib	20 Swinging boom fore	downhaul
3 Fore topgallant stay	12 Inner jib stay	guy lead block	26 Fore topmast staysail
4 Flying jib tack	13 Inner jib tack	21 Jib boom	sheet
5 Flying jib downhaul	14 Inner jib downhaul	22 Bowsprit	27 Fore stay
6 Flying jib	15 Inner jib	23 Fore topmast stay	28 Pinrail for staysails'
7 Flying jib boom	16 Flying jib boom guy	24 Fore topmast staysail	downhauls
8 Outer jib stay	17 Outer jib boom guy	tack	29 Whisker boom
9 Outer jib tack	18 Inner jib boom guy		30 Flying jib sheet
			31 Outer jib sheet

32 Inner jib sheet	39 Inner martingale
33 Fore topmast staysail	(stay)
sheet	40 Middle martingale
34 Pinrail	(stay)
35 Bowsprit shroud	41 Outer martingale
36 Martingale backrope	(stay)
(Martingale guy)	42 Foot rope
37 Bobstay	43 Bitts
38 Martingale or Dolphin	44 Capstan working the
striker	windlass
	45 Cathead

DETAILS OF MAINMAST AND MAINYARD OF A SNOW, ABOUT 1800

1	Mainmast	6	Main rigging	11	Main topsail	16	Mainyard footrope	21	Topsail sheet
2	Mainyard		or shrouds	12	Trysail	17	Mainyard stirrups	22	Topsail clewline
3	Main top	7	Futtock shrouds	13	Mainyard sling	18	Main clewgarnet	23	Topsail bowline bridle
4	Trysail mast	8	Topmast shrouds	14	Main lift	19	Reef tackle	24	Fore topsail brace
5	Trysail gaff	9	Mainstay	15	Main brace	20	Reef earing	25	Trysail brails
		10	Mainsail						

DETAILS OF MAINMAST HEAD, SHIP OF THE LINE, 1750

1 Mainmast	5 Heel of topmast	9 Parrel tackle
2 Trestle trees	6 Main cap	10 Main rigging or
3 Maintop	7 Mainyard	shrouds
4 Lower masthead	8 Main parrel	11 Mainstay
		12 Spring stay

13 Futtock shrouds	17 Main footrope
14 Topmast shrouds	18 Main clewgarnet
15 Mizzen topmast stay	19 Main topsail sheet
16 Main lift	20 Main jeers

RIGGING OF OLDER STEAMERS

A, B

Steamer from about 1890, rigged as a three-masted topsail schooner

A Fore topmast staysail
B Fore staysail
C Foresail; Boom foresail
D Topsail
E Topgallant sail
F Main staysail
G Mainsail
H Main gaff topsail
I Mizzen staysail
J Mizzen
K Mizzen gaff topsail

1 Foremast
2 Mainmast
3 Mizzenmast
4 Fore topmast
5 Fore topgallant mast
6 Main topmast
7 Main topgallant mast
8 Mizzen topmast
9 Fore yard
10 Topsail yard

11 Topgallant yard
12 Fore boom
13 Fore gaff
14 Main boom
15 Main gaff
16 Mizzen boom
17 Mizzen gaff
18 Fore topmast stay
19 Fore stay
20 Main stay

21 Main topmast stay
22 Main topgallant stay
23 Mizzen stay
24 Mizzen topmast stay
25 Fore braces
26 Topsail braces
27 Topgallant braces
28 Fore boom topping lift
29 Main boom topping lift

30 Mizzen boom topping lift
31 Fore vang
32 Main vang
33 Mizzen vang
34 Boom foresail sheet
35 Main sheet
36 Mizzen sheet
37 Flagstaff
38 Pole compass
39 Ventilator
40 Anchor davit

C *Patent reefing topsails were not unusual in the old steamers carrying sails, because of the possibility of reefing without a man leaving the deck*

1 Foresail
2 Topsail with Collin's and Pinkney's Patent (3)
4 Topgallant sail
5 Bermuda-type trysail traveling on a bar abaft the mast

RIGGING OF MODERN SHIPS

A *Electric deck crane*
1 Crane post
2 Electric equipment platform
3 Turning rim
4 Crane jib
5 Maneuvering stand
6 Topping motor
7 Hoisting motor
8 Slewing motor
9 Topping rope
10 Hoisting rope
11 Slack rope switch

12 Triple sheave block
13 Triple sheave block
14 Weight and swivel
15 Chain
16 Cargo hook
17 Electric light
18 Cage guard

B *Cargo vessel with deck cranes*

C *Rigging and derrick arrangement*
1 Foremast
2 Signal stay
3 Topmast stay
4 Masthead light
5 Outrigger
6 Crow's nest
7 Shrouds
8 5-ton booms
9 20-ton heavy boom
10 Topping and cargo winches

11 5-ton boom, gooseneck
12 Boom band
13 Topping lift block
14 Topping lift
15 Cargo hoist block
16 Cargo fall
17 Cargo hook
18 Topping lift and cargo fall heel blocks
19 5-ton boom guy
20 Heavy boom heel fitting
21 Boom head eye plate

22 Four-fold topping lift tackle
23 Mast band
24 Preventer stays
25 Topping lift and cargo fall block
26 Topping lift hauling part (wire)
27 Topper
28 Topper block
29 Cargo fall hauling part
30 Cargo fall sheave
31 Four-fold cargo tackle
32 20-ton cargo hook

D *Goal-post mast, pair mast*
1 King post
2 Transverse girder
3 Boom (behind post)
4 Gooseneck fitting
5 Band for lashing boom
6 Topmast
7 Topmast shrouds
8 Masthead light

Opposite is a 1492 nao; it is Columbus' SANTA MARIA and it introduces the section about sails. The color in the picture illustrates the fact that the chapter deals with flags as well.

THE SAIL

BY SAM SVENSSON

The oldest sail we know is the square sail. For many thousands of years no other types were used. The distinguishing feature of the square sail is that the same side is always turned to the wind. This is a simple, fundamental principle, and none of the aerodynamic inventions of recent years have changed the square sail or influenced its value for sailing on the high seas.

The fore-and-aft sail, which can face into the wind with either side, is a more recent development. What aerodynamics could not do for the square sail it has succeeded in doing for the fore-and-aft sail. The latter is very effective in close-hauled sailing and is superior for use while cruising. Today it is the sail most used for sport sailing among off-shore islands where winds are variable and the water is smooth. Because the fore-and-aft sail always has its forward bolt rope as the windward edge and the leech as the leeward edge, it can be cut with a favorable curvature. The square sail, on the other hand, has the starboard or port leech alternately as the windward edge, resulting in a different curvature. The value of the modern fore-and-aft sail on the wind is, however, outweighed by the advantages of the more secure square sail in running before the wind in stormy and high seas. Almost all sailing on the high seas has been done with the square sail. The oldest known reproduction of a boat equipped with a sail is painted on an Egyptian clay urn from the predynastic period. Estimated to be from about 4000 B.C., it could actually be even older. Furthermore, the evidence is not conclusive that this painting shows the world's first sail. Past cultures of which we have no knowledge may very well have had sailing vessels thousands of years before.

Contemporary writings and pictures prove that the sailors of ancient lands in the eastern Mediterranean used sails.

In the twenty-seventh chapter of Ezekiel, the ships of Tyrus are described as having cedar masts from Lebanon, gay, embroidered sails of fine Egyptian linen, and awnings of blue and purple cloth from the Isles of Elisha. The decoration of the sails indicates that they were used both for propulsion and as a means of identification.

We have no record of when the art of sailing was brought to Scandinavia, but by the Viking Age it was certainly hundreds, perhaps even thousands, of years old. Early Nordic sails were made of homespun wool, and lacked the durability of linen sail. The cloth would stretch under the force of the wind, and the large sail would sag more and more until it burst. To strengthen the sail and hold it more evenly, a supporting net was fastened to the forward side. The net, often of a different color than the sail, was either of rope, of cloth bands, or of interwoven sennit. The foot of the sail was held down by a number of sheets, forming bridles, all to hold the sail flatter. By the Viking Age, linen sails were in use on larger ships. These sails could be set flatter, making for better sailing on the wind. The long journeys made by the Vikings in European waters and over the Atlantic Ocean would have been impossible, if their ships had not been able to sail with all kinds of wind. At the dawn of Swedish history, the cruising ability of the ships of the time is illustrated in the saga of the King of the Sveas, Erik Väderhatt, who, according to history, could turn the wind so that he never had a headwind.

The majority of ships continued to have only one mast and a single sail for many years. Only after the later Middle Ages did larger ships commonly appear with two or three masts and sails — one sail on each mast. By the end of the 15th century, however, a new sail was set at the head of the mainmast. It was originally

very small, and was handled by the men in the top (an early masthead castle). It derived its name, the topsail, from this position. Another sail was added under the bowsprit; this was called the spritsail or blind, as it blocked the view ahead. Eventually a topsail was also added to the foremast. By the middle of the 16th century, then, a large three-masted ship carried six sails: the spritsail under the bowsprit, two sails on the foremast, two sails on the mainmast, and one sail on the mizzenmast. The sail on the mizzenmast was always a triangular lateen sail at this time.

The origin of the lateen sail is unknown. At the fall of the Roman Empire in 476 A.D., all ships had square sails. After that, sources of information on ships and navigation in the Mediterranean are not available for several hundreds of years. Not until the end of the 9th century do Greek manuscripts show some miniatures of ships with triangular sails under an inclined yard. Even today these sails are called lateen sails. These were probably introduced into the Mediterranean by the Arabs, but no one knows whether their origin is Arabian or Polynesian. Up to the 13th century the lateen sail was in use exclusively along the Mediterranean. But from that time on, the square sail began to make a comeback under western European impetus. The lateen sail was used, at this time, along the whole European coastline, especially as a mizzen on larger ships. It probably reached the Baltic by the latter half of the 15th century, about the same time as the carvel or smooth-sided shipbuilding technique came along. Down to the middle of the 18th century the lateen sail was in general international use as the mizzen. It was then replaced by the gaff mizzen. The coastal galleys of the Swedish navy continued to employ lateen sails as long as these ships were in use, the last one being built in 1749. But the development of sail went in the opposite direction in small barges and boats, and in the Mediterranean, the Red Sea, and the Persian Gulf. The lateen sail can be seen on these craft even today.

As the lateen sail has to be set on the leeward side of the mast, it is not suitable for tacking with short boards in a narrow channel. The rule is that lateen-rigged craft wear, and the sail is taken around forward of the mast and sheeted on the new lee side when the craft is wearing. Large Arab dhows still sail in this same manner from the Persian Gulf to East African ports, as far down as Zanzibar. They never beat against the wind, but run to Africa in the favorable wind of the northeast monsoon and return with the southwest monsoon to the Persian Gulf. They are, therefore, limited to only one such round trip a year, the same as the Indian grain carriers that make only one voyage a year to Rangoon to pick up rice for Ceylon.

The lateen sail was the world's first fore-and-aft sail. While it enjoyed great popularity in the Near East and Mediterranean for a long time, other types of sail began to appear in Europe. We can follow this development especially well in Holland and Friesland.

During the 16th century, Holland became the world's most powerful maritime nation, replacing the sea power of the Hanseatic League. Using the rich Rhineland inland waterways, the Dutch had developed navigation with small ships in canals and rivers and in the shallow coastal waters between the islands. The inability to beat and especially to tack in a narrow channel, when using a square sail, created the need for new types of sail, and Dutch art records two new fore-and-aft sails, the spritsail and staysail. The former was a simple rectangular sail with one side laced to the mast and extended by a diagon-

ally placed sprit. The sail was found to be very practical, and, as a result, it became the most commonly used sail in small sailing boats of Northern Europe. It was eventually used in larger craft as well, and is now best known on the Thames River barges, which still use it today.

With the spritsail set abaft the mast, there was an empty space under the stay on the forward side of the mast, and it was only natural to set a triangular sail on that stay before the mast. By the middle of the first half of the 16th century, boats with a spritsail and fore staysail were in use in Holland. The development of the fore staysail was followed by a new staysail called the jib, which was set on a jib boom outside the stem. These staysails were soon in general use in small vessels in Western Europe, but it was not until the end of the 17th century that staysails appeared in the larger, square-sailed ships.

Another fore-and-aft sail, the lug sail, came to Europe somewhat later. The lug sail was a rectangular one that was hoisted with an inclined yard, with the halliard nearer the forward yardarm. Again there is evidence that the lug sail was known in the eastern Mediterranean about 100 A.D.

We are not sure whether the lug sail evolved from the lateen sail by cutting away the forward section or whether it came from the square sail by moving the halliard nearer one end of the yard and at the same time shifting the sail's tack amidships. The lug sail was used mostly in Western Europe, in the English and French waters of the English Channel. French fishermen and smugglers, as well as privateers and customs boats with sharp lines and fast hulls, were often rigged with lug sails; the type was sometimes called the *Chasse Marée*. English and Scottish

fishermen in the North Sea also employed the lug sail, until they gave up the use of sails. Sailing ship's boats, both in the merchant marine and the navy, generally had lug sails as well, most often in one-masted, but also in two- or three-masted, rigs.

There were two types of lug sails: the standing and the dipping. The tack of the dipping lug was made fast a little before the mast, near the stem. It was always set to the lee of the mast and had to be shifted to the new leeward side at every tack. A standing lug had the tack at the mast and could take the wind from either side, though it was most effective when the yard was on the lee side of the mast. In ancient times it was very common for the masts of fishing boats to have no shrouds, and one sailed only "on the wood," as it was called. The sail was set on the lee side of the mast, with the halliards leading to the weather quarter and serving as a backstay to sail on. Coming about, the sail was shifted to the new lee and the halliard to the new weather side.

In addition to the fore-and-aft sail on fishing boats and smaller vessels, the lateen sail in the Mediterranean, the lug sail in Western Europe, and the spritsail in Northern Europe, there were many small craft that still used square sails. The "Roslagen" sloops from Stockholm's archipelago used square sails until the end of the 18th century, as did the Norwegian "Nordland" yachts—for as long as they used sails.

The original square sail, which had served maritime navigation for several thousand of years, was entirely different from the various kinds of fore-and-aft sails. When ships became larger and masts taller, the number of sails on each mast also increased. After the middle of the 16th century the larger ships set a third sail, the topgallant sail, which was rigged above the topsail. In the beginning of the 17th century a square sail, the spritsail topsail, was rigged on a topmast at the end of the bowsprit. An impractical square sail, its mast was very badly stayed and often prone to damage. It remained in use on larger ships, however, for more than a hundred years, before it was replaced by a more practical staysail, the jib.

The first staysails on larger ships were set between the masts as the main staysail, the main topmast staysail, and the mizzen staysail. In addition, there was the fore topmast staysail, which was placed on a special stay from the fore topmast head and parallel with the fore topmast stay. This stay was actually so cluttered with blocks and running gear for the spritsail that the additional rigging for the new staysail caused many difficulties. The fore topmast staysail was, however, a more effective headsail than either of the square sails on the bowsprit, and at the beginning of the 18th century the spritsail topsail disappeared. It was replaced, as was said earlier, by a new staysail called the jib. This was set on a new spar, the jib boom, which was rigged on the extension of the bowsprit.

By the beginning of the 18th century rigging became more functional. The sails could be reefed effectively, and the rigging allowed for better bracing, which meant better sailing to windward. The studding sail, which on occasion was already used in the previous century, became more common. It was used, when running free, to increase the sail area, much as the modern spinnaker functions on sailing yachts.

Toward the end of the 18th century larger ships began to use a fourth square sail above the topgallant sail. It was called the royal. In men-of-war it was always set flying, i.e., it was set from the deck, and when furled, it was taken down on deck. But in merchant ships it became a standing sail with the royal yard left aloft.

An important improvement in types of sail was made at the beginning of the 19th century, as the jackstay on the yards came into use. The head of the sail was bent to the jackstay on the forward upper side of the yard instead of having lashings around the yard. This made the work easier when bending and unbending sail, and especially when furling sail. The sail could then be rolled up on top of the yards, where it could be easily secured under the gaskets. Without the jackstay on the yards, the larger steel ships of a later period could not have sailed with the small crews they had.

After the Napoleonic era larger ships were rigged with a fifth sail, the skysail, which was carried over the royal. It was never widely used, but was seen mostly at the

time of the clipper ships, in the middle of the century. Some clippers carried still another sail, the moonsail, usually set only on the mainmast. Exaggerations could always be found, and one of the most unusual occurs in a story of the English corvette hunting for slavers in the steaming heat and calm waters of the Bay of Benin. Seamen tell of it carrying a royal, skysail, moonsail, heaven poker, angel poker, and cloud disturber—all over the topgallant sail.

Expanding 19th century industry gave rigging a more delicate look. Mechanical improvements in the rigging also influenced the sails. Thimbles and clasp hooks were introduced, and, later, shackles. Both square sail halliards and sheets were made of chain. Previously, the clews of square sails had been part of the bolt rope, which formed an eye in which the sheet and clewline were fastened. It now became common to put a thimble in the clew, and later to lead a cringle from the eye. Still later, a wrought-iron clew was spliced into the bolt ropes. In larger ships, with double topsail sheets, the clew was formed by a stropped block through which the sheet was reeved. The sheet was still made of hemp. In navy ships, where working the sails quickly became more and more important, all running gear was equipped with toggles, so that bowlines, buntlines, clewlines, and sheets could be let go in just a few seconds and a topsail shifted in just a few minutes.

When large ships began to be built of iron and then of steel, during the last half of the century, the standing rigging and then the running gear was made of wire. Even the sails were influenced. The huge square sails were given both leech and foot ropes of wire, and a bolt rope of wire could be used for foot and leech on the staysail but not for the luff, as this had to be folded along the stay when the sail was hauled down.

In addition to the fore-and-aft sails already mentioned—the lateen sail, spritsail, staysail, and lug sail—there is still another, the gaff sail, that gradually came to dominate all the others. It evolved from the spritsail by means of shortening the sprit, raising it, and fastening it to the sail's head. To keep it in place, with the forward end against the mast, the end was shaped as a throat or gaff with a branch fork, which partly covered the mast and gave both the spar and the sail its name, the gaff. To be able to hoist the gaff sail the mast had to be made higher than the sail, so that the gaff's halliards, the inner throat halliard, and the outer peak halliard could be fastened above the gaff.

Pictures of the gaff sail appear later than those of the spritsail, but also go as far back as the middle of the

17th century. Slowly, the gaff sail won out over the other fore-and-aft sails. Mail packets and other semi-official craft, which sailed with mail and passengers between specified ports, revenue cutters, the larger pilot boats, and similar craft were among the first to use the gaff sail. During the 18th century, smaller merchant ships and warships began more often to be rigged with the gaff sail. Various types of early schooners and sloops all had gaff sails.

During the 19th century, larger merchant ships, for example, the three-masted fore-and-aft schooners and barkentines, began to employ the gaff rig. Particularly in North America, by the end of the century, multi-masted fore-and-aft schooners began to show up. Many were four- or five-masted, several six-masted, and one was seven-masted. Some of them were extremely large sailing vessels that required steam winches to hoist their large gaff sails. They were at their best sailing on the wind in calm coastal waters; but they were difficult to run before the wind in hard weather. When they were used on deep-water voyages, their performance was usually much poorer than that of the square-riggers.

The gaff sail, however, soon became the most important sail for pleasure yachts. By the 17th century the Dutch, English, and even the Swedes had gaff-rigged pleasure yachts. With the development of sport sailing and yacht clubs in the maritime nations, the gaff-rigged cutter became more and more popular; though it was sometimes surpassed in size by two- and three-masted, gaff-rigged pleasure schooners. At the beginning of the 20th century the gaff sail was almost universally used in the yachting field.

Here, aerodynamic research performed a great service for sport sailing. As a result of new inventions, the wide gaff sail with a long boom is now almost as rare as the square sail. The only sail that has survived the extensive use of the motor yacht is the tall, narrow, gaffless boom sail, known as the Bermuda sail. Two hundred years ago fishermen in Bermuda were using a triangular mainsail without a gaff, but with a long boom. The modern yacht uses a sail which has only the name in common with that original Bermuda sail.

DIFFERENT SAILS

1 Spritsails
2 Standing lug sail
3 Gaff sail
4 Gunter rig
5 Bermuda sail
6 Staysail rig
7 Lateen sails
8 Square sail

SAILS OF A FOUR-MASTED BARK

(Herzogin Cecilie)
This four-masted bark was built in 1902 by Rickmers ship yard at Bremerhaven for the Norddeutscher Lloyd at Bremen. It was a big sailing vessel of 3,242 gross tons or 4,350 dw.

The Norddeutscher Lloyd, a large shipowner and in Germany second only to the Hamburg—America Line, employed the Herzogin Cecilie to train cadets as officers for their own fleet of ships. In addition

to the officers, teachers, and a skeleton crew of tradesmen and seamen, she was fitted out to carry ninety cadets. She had the best possible equipment, but with plenty of man power on board to pull

the braces she was rigged without any brace winches, as was customary at that time in big sailing ships of this class. She was a good sailer and made many excellent voyages. During World War 1 she was

interned at Coquimbo, Chile. After the war she brought a cargo of nitrate to Ostend, and was there allocated to the French government. In November, 1921, she was purchased by Gustaf Erikson, Marie-

hamn, and under his flag was employed chiefly in the Australian grain trade. She foundered on April 25, 1936, off Salcombe, Devonshire, after running aground in heavy fog.

SAILS OF A FOUR-MASTED BARK

1 Flying jib	9 Fore upper top-	14 Main sail, main	19 Main royal	24 Mizzen lower topsail	29 Jigger staysail
2 Outer jib	gallant sail	course	20 Mizzen topmast	25 Mizzen upper topsail	30 Jigger topmast
3 Inner jib	10 Fore royal	15 Main lower topsail	staysail	26 Mizzen lower top-	staysail
4 Fore topmast	11 Main topmast	16 Main upper topsail	21 Mizzen topgallant	gallant sail	31 Jigger topgallant
staysail	staysail	17 Main lower top-	staysail	27 Mizzen upper top-	staysail
5 Fore sail, fore course	12 Main topgallant	gallant sail	22 Mizzen royal staysail	gallant sail	32 Lower spanker
6 Fore lower topsail	staysail	18 Main upper top-	sail	28 Mizzen royal	33 Upper spanker
7 Fore upper topsail	13 Main royal staysail	gallant sail	23 Crossjack, mizzen		34 Gaff topsail
8 Fore lower top-			course		
gallant sail					

SAILS IN VARIOUS SAILING VESSELS

A *Four-masted fore-and-aft schooner*	12 Mizzen gaff topsail	10 Main lower topsail	8 Mainsail	8 Fore topgallant sail	20 Mizzen topmast staysail
	13 Jigger or spanker	11 Main upper topsail	9 Main topsail	9 Fore royal	21 Main spencer
1 Flying jib	14 Jigger gaff topsail	12 Main topgallant sail'	10 Main topgallant sail	10 Main royal staysail	22 Crossjack
2 Outer jib	B *Brig*	13 Main royal	D *Full-rigged four-masted ship*	11 Main topgallant staysail	23 Mizzen lower topsail
3 Inner jib	1 Flying jib	14 Trysail		12 Main topmast staysail	24 Mizzen upper topsail
4 Fore staysail	2 Jib	C *Two-topsail schooner*	1 Flying jib	13 Mainsail	25 Mizzen topgallant sail
5 Square foresail	3 Fore topmast staysail	1 Flying jib	2 Outer jib	14 Main lower topsail	26 Mizzen royal
6 Raffee	4 Foresail	2 Outer jib	3 Inner jib	15 Main upper topsail	27 Mizzen spencer
7 Foresail	5 Fore lower topsail	3 Inner jib	4 Fore topmast staysail	16 Main topgallant sail	28 Jigger lower topsail
8 Fore gaff topsail	6 Fore upper topsail	4 Fore staysail	5 Foresail	17 Main royal	29 Jigger upper topsail
9 Mainsail	7 Fore topgallant sail	5 Foresail	6 Fore lower topsail	18 Mizzen royal staysail	30 Jigger topgallant sail
10 Main gaff topsail	8 Fore royal	6 Fore topsail	7 Fore upper topsail	19 Mizzen topgallant staysail	31 Jigger royal
11 Mizzen	9 Mainsail	7 Fore topgallant sail			32 Spanker

SAILS IN VARIOUS SAILING VESSELS

A Three-masted staysail schooner	B Ketch	C Sloop	D Four-masted barkentine	
1 Flying jib	1 Flying jib	1 Jib topsail	1 Flying jib	10 Main staysail
2 Jib	2 Outer jib	2 Jib	2 Outer jib	11 Middle staysail
3 Fore staysail	3 Inner jib	3 Fore staysail	3 Inner jib	12 Main topmast staysail
4 Fore trysail	4 Fore staysail	4 Square foresail	4 Fore topmast staysail	13 Mainsail
5 Main staysail	5 Mainsail	5 Mainsail	5 Foresail	14 Main gaff topsail
6 Main trysail	6 Main gaff topsail	6 Gaff topsail	6 Fore lower topsail	15 Mizzen topmast staysail
7 Mizzen staysail	7 Mizzen		7 Fore upper topsail	16 Mizzen
8 Jib-headed spanker	8 Mizzen gaff topsail		8 Fore lower topgallant sail	17 Mizzen gaff topsail
			9 Fore upper topgallant sail	18 Jigger topmast staysail
				19 Jigger or spanker
				20 Jigger gaff topsail

1 Lift by which the yard can be trimmed either way out of the horizontal. In port, this can be done independently of the yards above and to a considerable angle. At sea, when sails are set, the movement is restricted, but affects all the yards on the mast.

2 Buntline blocks under rim of top

3 Buntline blocks on yard seized to jack stay

4 Clewgarnet by which the clews of the sail are hauled up to the yardarms

5 Leech line

6 Outer buntline

7 Inner buntline

8 Middle buntline

9 Bull's eye sewn to the sail to lead the buntlines

10 Buntline hitch

11 Tacks leading forward

12 Sheets leading aft; the clews of the sail are trimmed to the wind by tacks and sheets

When the sail is to be furled, the tacks and sheets are let go and the sail is hauled up to the yard by the clewgarnets and buntlines. Then the men go aloft,

lie out on the yard, and roll up the sail tightly and secure it by tying the gaskets around yard and sail.

13 Gaskets

14 Braces leading aft, by which the yard is braced to different winds

1 Yardarm

2 Yardarm band

3 Lift shackled to yardarm band

4 Clewgarnet

5 Hauling out part of head earing

6 Round turns of head earing

7 Ring for head earing

8 Head of sail

9 Leech of sail

10 Robands, tied with a square knot

11 Jack stay

12 Clew of galvanized iron

13 Thimble for foot of sail

14 Thimble for leech

15 Shackle for sheet

16 Bull's-eye sewed into sail

17 Cringle on bolt rope with round thimble

TOPMAST, TOPSAIL, AND TOPGALLANT SAIL WITH RUNNING GEAR

1 Topgallant leech, port side
2 Topgallant clew
3 Topgallant sheet
4 Topgallant clewline
5 Tabling on foot of topgallant sail
6 Flat seam between the cloths of the sail
7 Cloth of canvas, generally 2 feet wide
8 Topgallant buntline
9 Topmast crosstree
10 Upper topsail yard
11 Upper topsail yard parrel
12 Upper topsail yard tie
13 Sheave hole in topmast for the tie
14 Topsail tie gin block
15 Topsail halliard chain span
16 Topsail halliard tackle
17 Topsail halliard lead block
18 Upper topsail brace pendant
19 Upper topsail brace runner
20 Upper topsail brace falls
21 Leading block of upper topsail brace
22 Topmast
23 Lower mast
24 Topsail yard lift
25 Topsail yard downhaul
26 Foot rope of upper topsail yard
27 Stirrups to support foot rope
28 Yardarm horse
29 Yardarm
30 Yardarm band
31 Jack stay to which sail is bent

THE SQUARE SAIL

A *Square-rigged mast, seen from aft*

1 Deck
2 Lower mast with top
3 Topmast with cross-trees
4 Topgallant mast
5 Royal mast
6 Pole
7 Lower yard
8 Lower topsail yard
9 Upper topsail yard
10 Topgallant yard
11 Royal yard
12 Lower sheet
13 Clewgarnet
14 Topsail clewline
15 Lower topsail buntline, shown in broken lines forward of sail
16 Topsail halliard, tie
17 Topsail halliard, spanner
18 Topsail halliard, tackle or falls
19 Upper topsail brace
20 Topsail downhaul
21 Topsail lift
22 Upper topsail yard footrope
23 Upper topsail yardarm horse
24 Topgallant sheet
25 Topgallant clewline
26 Topgallant buntline
27 Topgallant lift
28 Topgallant yard footrope
29 Royal lift
30 Royal yard footrope
31 Royal buntline

B *Plan of fife rail at mizzenmast of a big sailing ship*

1 Section of mast with spider hoop
2 Mast coat at deck
3 U-shaped fife rail with belaying pins
4 Bilge pumps on deck
5 Pump axle with fly-wheels
6 Detachable pump cranks stowed on fife rail
7 Chain wheel for messenger from steam winch
8 Manhole from deck to pump well
9 Fresh water pump from tanks below deck
10 Lower topsail sheet
11 Upper topsail sheet
12 Crossjack clewgarnet
13 Inner crossjack buntlines
14 Outer crossjack buntlines
15 Crossjack lift
16 Mizzen topgallant sheet
17 Main lower topgallant brace
18 Main upper topgallant brace
19 Jigger topmast staysail downhaul
20 Jigger topgallant staysail downhaul

A

B

C

RUNNING RIGGING OF THE SQUARE SAILS OF A FOUR-MASTED BARK

A *Braces and sheets*	9 Main upper topsail	17 Mizzen upper top-	25 Main sheet	33 Mizzen upper topsail	B *Buntlines, clewlines,*
1 Fore brace	brace	gallant brace	26 Main lower topsail	sheet	*and downhauls*
2 Fore lower topsail	10 Main lower topgallant	18 Mizzen royal brace	sheet	34 Mizzen lower top-	1 Fore clewgarnet
brace	brace	19 Fore sheet	27 Main upper topsail	gallant sheet	2 Fore lower topsail
3 Fore upper topsail	11 Main upper topgallant	20 Fore lower topsail	sheet	35 Mizzen upper top-	clewline
brace	brace	sheet	28 Main lower topgallant	gallant sheet	3 Fore upper topsail
4 Fore lower topgallant	12 Main royal brace	21 Fore upper topsail	sheet	36 Mizzen royal sheet	downhaul
brace	13 Crossjack brace	sheet	29 Main upper topgallant	37 Fore tack	4 Fore lower topgallant
5 Fore upper topgallant	14 Mizzen lower topsail	22 Fore lower topgallant	sheet	38 Main tack	clewline
brace	brace	sheet	30 Main royal sheet	39 Crossjack tack	5 Fore upper topgallant
6 Fore royal brace	15 Mizzen upper topsail	23 Fore upper topgallant	31 Crossjack sheet		downhaul
7 Main brace	brace	sheet	32 Mizzen lower topsail		6 Fore royal clewline
8 Main lower topsail	16 Mizzen lower top-	24 Fore royal sheet	sheet		7 Main clewgarnet
brace	gallant brace				

Continued

Since this is an outline sketch only, see also page 245

Continued

8 Main lower topsail clewline
9 Main upper topsail downhaul
10 Main lower topgallant clewline
11 Main upper topgallant downhaul
12 Main royal clewline
13 Crossjack clewgarnet
14 Mizzen lower topsail clewline
15 Mizzen upper topsail downhaul

16 Mizzen lower top-gallant clewline
17 Mizzen upper top-gallant downhaul
18 Mizzen royal clewline
19 Fore buntlines
20 Fore lower topsail buntlines
21 Fore upper topsail buntlines
22 Fore lower topgallant buntlines
23 Fore upper topgallant buntlines

24 Fore royal buntlines
25 Main buntlines
26 Main lower topsail buntlines
27 Main upper topsail buntlines
28 Main lower topgallant buntlines
29 Main upper topgallant buntlines
30 Main royal buntlines
31 Crossjack buntlines
32 Mizzen lower topsail buntlines

33 Mizzen upper topsail buntlines
34 Mizzen lower top-gallant buntlines
35 Mizzen upper top-gallant buntlines
36 Mizzen royal buntlines

C *Mizzenmast with braces leading to a brace winch at the foot of jiggermast*

Since this is an outline sketch only, see also page 245

TOPSAIL HALLIARDS AND WINCHES

A *Topsail halliard winch*
1 Flywheel with removable handle, which was removed after the sail was hoisted so as to be out of the way
2 Worm gear
3 Grooved barrel for the halliard, tapered to increase power as the yard ascends
4 Brake

5 Wheel with threaded shaft to control the brake. When the topsail yard was lowered, the brake was eased off and the flywheel was given a start with a push. This set the barrel revolving; the downward speed was regulated by the brake.

Continued

Continued

B *Topsail halliard of a barkentine*
1 End of chain span across the deck
2 Mousing on hook
3 Moving block, double
4 Becket, in one with the straps
5 Fall, two-fold purchase rove to advantage
6 Pin rail
7 Belaying pin
8 Main rail

C *Brace winch invented by Captain J. C. Jarvis*

of Tayport, Scotland. The winch controls the lower brace and the two topsail braces, one winch for each mast. The winch has three axles, each with two barrels, and is so arranged with cogwheels that when the winch is turned, braces on one side pay out as those on the other side wind on.
1 Weather side brace paid out
2 Lee side brace hove in

1 Lower mast, foremast
2 Top
3 Cap
4 Topmast
5 Topmast crosstree
6 Lower foreyard
7 Lower topsail yard
8 Upper topsail yard
9 Lower studding sail yard
10 Topmast studding sail boom
11 Topmast studding sail yard

12 Topgallant studding sail boom
13 Fore course, foresail
14 Lower topsail
15 Upper topsail
16 Topgallant sail
17 Lower studding sail
18 Topmast studding sail
19 Topgallant studding sail
20 Lower rigging or shrouds
21 Futtock shrouds

22 Topmast rigging or shrouds
23 Lower yard footrope
24 Lower topsail sheet of chain
25 Inner lower studding sail halliard
26 Outer lower studding sail halliard
27 Topmast studding sail sheet
28 Topmast studding sail tack
29 Lower topsail brace

30 Lower topsail clewline
31 Lower topsail lift
32 Upper topsail sheet
33 Upper topsail clewline
34 Upper topsail brace
35 Upper topsail lift
36 Topgallant studding sail sheet
37 Topgallant studding sail tack
38 Topmast studding sail halliard
39 Topgallant sheet
40 Topgallant clewline

SQUARE SAILS AND STUDDING SAILS

A *Studding sails*
1 Outline sketch showing studding sails and their spars and rigging, looking aft
2 Band on the yardarm for the studding sail boom

B *Square sail by the Rägener system*
Many inventors have tried to improve upon the traditional square rig, which evolved empirically from centuries of experience gained the hard way. None did much to improve the old sailing ship, and this system by Rägener, with trussed yards and sails running on horizontal slides and brailed in to the mast, never got beyond the drawing board.

A

B

PATENT SELF-REEFING TOPSAILS

A *Cunningham's patent*

1 Revolving topsail yard
2 Bight of chain topsail tie
3 Topmast
4 Topsail yard parrel
5 Chafing spar to protect the sail when reefed
6 Roller lead for tie
7 Bolt for downhaul tackle
8 T-shaped bolt for the bonnet
9 Yardarm hoop within which the yard works
10 Bolt for topsail yard lifts
11 Leading block for topgallant sheet
12 Shackle to take the brace
13 Downhaul tackle
14 Twin runners of topsail halliards
15 Twin tackles of topsail halliards

B *Colling's & Pinkney's patent*

1 Topsail yard
2 Parrel
3 Rolling spar
4 Iron drum end of rolling spar
5 Yardarm hoop
6 Arm carrying reefing halliard block
7 Cheek block for topgallant sheet
8 Parrel crutch with lignum vitae rollers
9 Lignum vitae rollers
10 Topsail
11 Lead block for reefing halliards
12 Topsail yardarm

DIFFERENT RIGGING OF LOWER SQUARE SAILS

A *Big square-rigged sailing ships could, sometimes, set a three-cornered mainsail or crossjack. Such a sail could be carried in a gale long after a square sail had to be taken in, but this advantage was counteracted by the fact that the three-cornered sail gave less spread of canvas in a moderate wind. In A the numbers indicate:*

1 Lower yard
2 Three-cornered sail
3 Buntlines
4 Tackle sheet in front of mast

B *A four-masted bark under all sail, setting a three-cornered crossjack, while the mainsail is drawn double showing both a square sail and a three-cornered sail*

C *A course, say, mainsail, clewed up to the yardarm, as seen from forward*

1 Lower mast
2 The top
3 Lower yard
4 Lifts

5 Lower topsail sheet, sail clewed up to the yardarm
6 The sail, say, mainsail
7 Clewgarnets
8 Buntlines
9 Leechlines
10 Tacks and sheets
11 Gaskets

D *A course, mainsail, clewed up in the bunt as seen from forward*

1 The sail
2 Reef band
3 Clewgarnets abaft the sail
4 Buntlines
5 Leechlines
6 Gaskets
7 Lower topsail sheet, sail clewed up in the bunt

E *A mainsail clewed up in the bunt as seen from aft*

1 Clewgarnets
2 Buntlines
3 Leechlines
4 Sheet

F *A mainsail with the clews hauled up as seen from aft*

1 Clewgarnets
2 Buntlines
3 Leechlines
4 Sheets

THE GAFF SAIL (FROM PAASCH)

A	Gaff sail					
1	Throat	7	Luff	14	Second reef band	
2	Peak	8	Luff rope	15	Balance reef band	
3	Tack	9	Leech	16	Throat cringle	
4	Clew	10	Leech rope	17	Peak cringle	
5	Head	11	Foot	18	Tack cringle	
6	Headrope	12	Foot rope	19	Clew cringle	
		13	First reef band	20	Reef cringles	
				21	Reef points	

B *A spanker, which sets under a standing gaff and brails in to the mast, (leeches and cringles made as in A)*

1	Half a cloth tabling on the luff	4	Sheet patch
2	Folding on the after leech with three holes to take the brails	5	Tack patch
		6	Peak patch
3	Lead of brails across the sail	7	Detail of peak cringle

THE GAFF SAIL

1 Gaff	7 Sheet band	13 Spiral lacing	19 Outer jibstay	25 Fore throat halliards	31 Foot of sail
2 Head earing	8 Sheet	14 Mainstay	20 Outer jib halliard	26 Trestletrees	32 Boom
3 Peak halliards	9 Distance line	15 Cap	21 Inner jibstay	27 Topmast	33 Seizings
4 Clew shackle	10 Hoops	16 Fore peak halliards	22 Inner jib halliard	28 Cheeks	34 Marline hitched lacing
5 Boom end	11 Bolt rope on luff of sail	17 Peak halliard block	23 Forestay	29 Mast battens	35 Wire jack stay
6 Reef cringle	12 Mast	18 Foremast head	24 Fore staysail halliard	30 Foremast	36 Eyelet hole for lacing

A *The peak halliards and topping lifts of the gaff sails on board a three-masted fore-and-aft schooner*

1 Fore peak halliard
2 Main peak halliard
3 Mizzen peak halliard
4 Fore topping lift
5 Main topping lift
6 Mizzen topping lift

B *The throat halliards and sheets of the gaff sails on board a three-masted fore-and-aft schooner*

1 Fore throat halliard
2 Main throat halliard
3 Mizzen throat halliard
4 Fore sheet
5 Main sheet
6 Mizzen sheet or spanker sheet

C *Different gaff sails*
1 Upper and lower spanker of the five-masted bark *Potosi*
2 Jigger of the four-masted bark *Archibald Russell*

3 Spanker of a big American fore-and-aft schooner. The vertical ropes (4) from the topping lift are called lazy jacks.

FORE-AND-AFT TOPSAILS

A *Jib-headed gaff topsail*
1 Head
2 Clew
3 Tack
4 Mast hoops
5 Clewline

6 Sheet
7 Throat halliard of
   the gaff sail
8 Peak halliard of
   the gaff sail

The gaff topsail is car-
ried on the lee side of
the peak halliard and
the tack leads down to
deck on the weather
side of the gaff. When
the ship is put about,
one man has to go aloft
and shift the sail over
to the new lee side.

B *Another way of rigging*
   the gaff topsail with
   two clewlines

C *Different types of*
   fore-and-aft topsails
1 Lateen topsail from the
   middle of the 16th
   century

2 Square gaff topsail bent
   to a short yard
3 Jackyard topsail of a
   cutter from the 1890's

STAYSAIL

STAYSAIL

1 Head	6 Leech	11 Head cringle	17 Horse	21 Luff rope
2 Tack	7 Leech rope	12 Tack cringle	18 Shrouds	22 Wooden staysail hanks
3 Clew	8 Foot	13 Clew ring	19 Hemp stay	23 Wire stay
4 Luff	9 Foot rope	14 Staysail boom	20 Lacing	24 Iron staysail hanks
5 Luff rope	10 Girth band	15 Fore staysail sheet		
		16 Preventer sheet		

RUNNING GEAR OF STAYSAILS IN A FOUR-MASTED BARK, DIFFERENT TYPES OF STAYSAILS

A *Sheets*
1 Fore royal staysail sheets
2 Flying jib sheets
3 Outer jib sheets
4 Inner jib sheets
5 Fore topmast staysail sheets
6 Main royal staysail sheet
7 Main topgallant staysail sheet
8 Main topmast staysail sheet
9 Mizzen royal staysail sheet
10 Mizzen topgallant staysail sheet
11 Mizzen topmast staysail sheet
12 Jigger topgallant staysail sheet
13 Jigger topgallant staysail sheet
14 Jigger staysail sheet

B *Halliards and downhauls*
1 Fore royal staysail halliards
2 Flying jib halliards
3 Outer jib halliards
4 Inner jib halliards
5 Fore topmast staysail halliards
6 Main royal staysail halliards
7 Main topgallant staysail halliards
8 Main topmast staysail halliards
9 Mizzen royal staysail halliards
10 Mizzen topgallant staysail halliards
11 Mizzen topmast staysail halliards
12 Jigger topgallant staysail halliards
13 Jigger topgallant staysail halliards
14 Jigger staysail halliards
15 Fore royal staysail downhaul
16 Flying jib downhaul
17 Outer jib downhaul
18 Inner jib downhaul
19 Fore topmast staysail downhaul
20 Main royal staysail downhaul
21 Main topgallant staysail downhaul
22 Main topmast staysail downhaul
23 Mizzen royal staysail downhaul
24 Mizzen topgallant staysail downhaul
25 Mizzen topmast staysail downhaul
26 Jigger topgallant staysail downhaul
27 Jigger topgallant staysail downhaul
28 Jigger staysail downhaul

C *Different shapes of staysails*

BONNETS AND REEFS

A A merchant ship from the first half of the 17th century. Additional sails, called bonnets, are laced to the foot of her courses and lateen mizzen. Sail area can be reduced by unlacing the bonnets.

1 Mizzen
2 Mizzen bonnet
3 Mainsail
4 Main bonnet
5 Foresail
6 Fore bonnet

B The bonnets were laced to the sails in such a way as to make the lacing spill itself once it was started; this made quick work of shortening sail

1 Lower sail
2 Bonnet
3 The clew of the sail seized to the earing of the bonnet
4 The leech rope of the bonnet, ending in a wall knot and stropped to the leech of the sail
5 Lacing of head of bonnet to foot of sail is made to spill once its stop is let go

C Enlargement of clew of sail, showing details

D Sectional view of a reefed sail
1 Foot of sail
2 Reef band
3 Reef point
4 Reef point knotted around reef with a reef knot
5 Rolled-up canvas in reef

SAIL DETAILS

A Norse Viking ship beating with a spar, known as a beatas, to hold the weather leech instead of a bowline; detail showing the spar's connection to sail

B Outline drawing of an American clipper close hauled on the port tack, with her weather bowlines picked out on her courses, topsails, and topgallant sails

C Detail of a bowline bridle
1 Bowline hitched to the dead block with a bowline
2 Long bridle
3 Short bridle
4 Bowline cringle in sail
5 Eyelet-holes in sail for short bridle

D Bark with double topsails, sailing by the wind under reefed upper topsails, lower topsails, and foresail

E Section of a yard showing a reefed sail
1 Yard
2 Jack stay
3 Stirrup
4 Sail below the reef
5 Reef band
6 Reefed part of sail
7 Reef point tied around yard and sail with a reef knot

BLOCKS OF DIFFERENT TYPES

1 Large modern triple block, with internal straps and side hook; parts of the straps go through the block and form the becket for the standing part of the fall

2 Triple block for a hemp strop, 19th century

3 Single block, side view and front view, for a hemp strop, 18th century

4 Dutch style yardarm sheet block for topsail sheet and lower lift, front view and side view, 17th century

5 Deadeye, 19th century

6 Clewgarnet block, side view and front view; this block has been turned on a lathe; medieval or 16th century

7 Fiddleblock, side view and front view, with two sheaves, 18th or 19th century

8 Fiddleblock, with external strap and hook, 19th century

9 Wire-stropped sheet block, with clip hooks and a cleat for the sheet, so as to make the sheet block travel on a horse, 20th century

10 Double block with a double strop and hook, for masthead pendant, 19th century

11 Triple fiddleblock, with external strap and thimble for splicing the pendant, 19th century

12 Snatch block, with external straps and a swivel hook, 19th century

A *Tackles (the number of loads indicates the increase of power for each tackle)*
1 Single whip
2 Runner
3 Gun tackle
4 Gun tackle rove to advantage
5 Luff tackle
6 Luff tackle rove to advantage
7 Double purchase

8 Double purchase rove to advantage
9 Winding tackle
10 Reversed winding tackle
11 Triple tackle
12 Reversed triple tackle
13 Four-by-three tackle
14 Three-by-four tackle
15 Four-fold tackle
16 Quadruple tackle

B *Different blocks with internal iron straps*
1 Single block with a ring
2 Fore-and-aft jib sheet block
3 Double block with sister hooks
4 Triple block with a shackle
5 Single block with loose swivel screw eye bolt

6 Double block with an eye
7 Double block with shackle and becket
8 Single block with stiff swivel jaws and becket
9 Double block with stiff swivel hook and becket
10 Triple block with stiff fixed front hook and becket

11 Double block with eye bolt and nut and becket
12 Single block with stiff jaws and becket
13 Triple block with loose side hook and becket
14 Single block with a solid eye for gaff bands

15 Triple block with loose swivel hook and becket
16 Double block with loose swivel jaws with guy eyes
17 Double block with stiff swivel jaws with guy eyes and becket

SOME OLD RIGGING DETAILS

A *Topsail halliard, end of 17th century*
1 Tie
2 Tackle
3 Lower lift

B *Wooden blocks without strops*

C *Chain plate with dead-eye*

D *Block for hemp strop*
1 Shell
2 Score for the strop
3 Sheave
4 Pin

E *Fiddleblock with one sheave smaller than the other*

F *Deadeye, turned in a shroud*
1 Deadeye
2 Shroud
3 Throat-seizing
4 End-seizing
5 Lanyard

G *Lower yardarm with topsail sheet block*
1 Lower yardarm
2 Topsail sheet block
3 Topsail sheet
4 Lower lift

TOOLS FOR SAIL-MAKING AND RIGGING WORK

1 Big sail needle, roping needle
2 Carved bullock's horn with tallow for holding needles
3 Prickers for small work
4 Marlinespikes for splicing wire
5 Sail-maker's palm
6 Splicing fids
7 Turning fids or heavers
8 Serving mallets

OLD TYPES OF SAILING SHIPS

1 Egyptian sea-going ship, about 1500 B.C.
2 Roman trader, about A.D. 200
3 Viking longship, A.D. 900
4 Norman ship from the 13th century

5 Hulk of the Hanseatic League, about 1470
6 Spanish caravel, about 1490
7 Spanish ship, nao, about 1490

8 English carrack, about 1500
9 Swedish kravel, galleon, 1550
10 North European boeier, 1560
11 West European galleon, 1590
12 Dutch flute, 1640

OLD TYPES OF SAILING SHIPS

13 Dutch pinnace, middle of 17th century

14 Swedish packet, 1690

15 72-gun ship, 1746

16 Merchantman, 1770

17 Hooker, second half of 18th century

18 Algerian chebec, 18th century

19 Swedish krayer, second half of 18th century

20 Swedish East Indiaman, 1786

21 Swedish snow, 1783

22 Swedish bark, 1792

23 Baltimore clipper, 1820

SOME ETHNOGRAPHICAL BOAT TYPES

1 Reed-boat from Lake Titicaca, South America
2 Boat from Lake Victoria
3 Koster boat from west coast of Sweden
4 Portuguese muleta
5 Small fishing boat from west coast of Sweden
6 Outrigger canoe from the South Pacific
7 Piragua from Tahiti
8 Norwegian jacht
9 Boat from East Pakistan
10 Boat from Kimari, India
11 Sloop from archipelago off Stockholm
12 Tartan, trading craft from western Mediterranean
13 Dutch barge
14 Boat from the Göta River, West Sweden
15 Fishing boat from the Åland Islands, Finland
16 Danish revenue cutter
17 Norfolk wherry
18 Turkish caique
19 Humber keel, Yorkshire

SOME ETHNOGRAPHICAL BOAT TYPES

20 Dutch koff
21 Boat from Bahia, Brazil
22 Bilancella, Italian
   fishing craft
23 Bovo, Sicilian coaster
24 Arabian dhow
25 Egyptian markab

26 Paduakan, coasting
   craft from Celebes
27 Scow schooner, New
   Zealand
28 Thames barge
29 Ketch, Åland Islands,
   Finland

30 Junk, Amoy, South
   China
31 Velocera, Sicilian,
   lateen-rigged
   barkentine
32 Old barge, Lake of
   Vänern, Sweden

DIFFERENT RIGS

1 Five-masted ship
2 Four-masted ship
3 Ship
4 Brig
5 Snow
6 Main topsail brigan-
tine
7 Five-masted bark
8 Four-masted bark
9 Bark

DIFFERENT RIGS

10 Brigantine or hermaph-
    rodite brig
11 Four-masted jackass
    bark
12 Jackass bark

13 Six-masted barkentine
14 Five-masted barkentine
15 Four-masted
    barkentine

16 Barkentine
17 Five-masted two-
    topsail schooner
18 Four-masted topsail
    schooner

19 Three-masted topsail
    schooner
20 Topsail schooner
21 Main-topsail schooner
    or two-topsail schooner

DIFFERENT RIGS

22 Seven-masted fore-and-aft schooner

The only seven-masted schooner ever built was the American schooner THOMAS W. LAWSON built at Quincy, Mass., 1902. According to a letter from the captain the masts were named as follows: Fore, Main, Mizzen, Number 4, Number 5, Number 6 and Spanker. This letter is kept in Peabody Museum, Salem, Mass.

23 Six-masted fore-and-aft schooner

24 Five-masted fore-and-aft schooner

25 Four-masted fore-and-aft schooner rigged with a flying foresail

26 Three-masted fore-and-aft schooner

27 Two-masted fore-and-aft schooner

28 Three-masted staysail schooner

29 Two-masted staysail schooner

DIFFERENT RIGS

30 Two-masted schooner
   with Bermuda
   mainsail
31 Ketch
32 Bermuda-rigged ketch
33 Gaff-rigged cutter

34 Baltic sloop
35 Launch rigged with
   dipping lugsails
36 Gunter-rigged gig

FLAGS

MERCHANT FLAGS

1 Norway	6 France	11 Greece	16 Panama	21 Brazil	26 Chile
2 Finland	7 Eire	12 Turkey	17 Honduras	22 Argentina	27 South Korea
3 West Germany	8 Portugal	13 Israel	18 Costa Rica	23 Mexico	28 Republic of South Africa
4 Belgium	9 Spain	14 Canada	19 Liberia	24 Colombia	29 India
5 Netherlands	10 Italy	15 New Zealand	20 Japan	25 Venezuela	30 China, Formosa

FIVE FLAGS

A Sweden
1 In the second half of the 16th century the present Swedish flag was not yet in use. Instead Swedish men-of-war flew a blue-and-white striped flag.
The pennant at the masthead, however, carried the three Swedish crowns.
2 The three-tongued blue flag of the fleet of the army, 1761-1813
3 The ensign of 1658, from the oldest preserved Swedish flag, now in Rijksmuseum, Amsterdam
4 Merchant flag, 1815-1844, with the canton of the Swedish-Norwegian Union
5 The ensign with the canton of the Union, 1844-1905
6 Merchant flag, after 1905

B Great Britain
1 Union flag
2 Cross of St. George
3 Cross of St. Andrew
4 Cross of St. Patrick
5 Merchant flag (red ensign)

C Denmark
According to a legend, the Danish flag fell from the sky in front of the army in 1219 and lead the army to victory. It is probably the oldest flag in the world, and has been Denmark's colors since the 14th century.

D United States of America
1 The U.S. flag of today. The stars represent the 50 states and the stripes the original 13 states.
2 The 13 stars of 1777
3 1795
4 1818
5 1846
6 1848
7 1912
No official design for placement of the stars existed before 1912

E Australia
The five stars in the field are the principal stars in the Southern Cross constellation. The large star below the canton is the symbolic "Commonwealth Star"

1 National flag
2 Merchant flag

FLAGS

A *House flags from sailing ship days*
1 The Hanseatic League, Lübeck (the Middle Ages)
2 The East India Company, London
3 Black Ball Line, New York (1816)
4 Enoch Train White Diamond Line, Boston (1820's)
5 Grinnell, Minturn & Co., New York, Swallow Tail Line for Liverpool
6 Grinnell, Minturn & Co., New York, Swallow Tail Line for London
7 Arthur Sewall, Bath, Me.
8 Alaska Packers Association, San Francisco
9 Money Wigram & Sons, London
10 George Thompson & Co., Aberdeen White Star Line, Aberdeen
11 John Willis & Son, London
12 Devitt & Moore, London

13 John Hardie & Co., Glasgow
14 Thomas Law & Co., Shire Line, Glasgow
15 John Stewart & Co., London
16 Andrew Weir & Co., Bank Line, Glasgow
17 Soc. Anon. Des Voiliers Nantais, Nantes
18 Ferdinand Laeisz, Hamburg
19 S. O. Stray & Co., Kristiansand
20 Gustaf Erikson, Mariehamn

B *Other house marks: Black Ball Packet* Besides flags, proud owners often had marks on the sails similar to the funnel marks of today. The Black Ball Line, New York, carried a black ball on the fore topsail, which was visible from far away.

C *Flags of a merchant ship*
1 Jack, often a small house flag or coat of arms, only flown in port

2 When in port abroad: the color of the country. In ports at home: when loading, the color of the country where bound, or when discharging, the color of the country from which the ship has arrived
3 Code flag, the Blue Peter, if vessel is to proceed to sea
4 Mail flag, if vessel carries mail

5 House flag
6 National colors, when in port
7 National colors, when at sea, if ship is fitted with an ensign gaff on the mainmast
D *Flags of man-of-war*
1 Union Jack
2 Naval flag
3 Commander's flag or pennant

A

B

HOUSE FLAGS OF TODAY

1 P & O Steam and Nav. Co., London, 1834
2 Cunard Steamship Co., Liverpool, 1840
3 Matson Nav. Co., San Francisco
4 United Fruit Co., Boston, New York
5 American President Line, San Francisco
6 United States Lines, New York
7 British India Co., London
8 Royal Mail Steam Packet Co., London

9 Pacific Steam Nav. Co., Liverpool
10 Canadian Pacific Railways Co., London
11 Blue Star Line, London
12 British Tankers Co., Ltd., London
13 Cie de Messageries Maritimes, Paris
14 Rotterdamsche Lloyd, Rotterdam
15 Hamburg American Line, Hamburg
16 Norddeutscher Lloyd, Bremen

17 Det Forenede Damp-skibselskab, Copenhagen
18 J. Lauritzen, Esbjerg
19 Norwegian American Line, Oslo
20 Wilhelm Wilhelmsen, Oslo
21 Swedish American Line, Gothenburg
22 Johnson Line, Stockholm
23 Nippon Yusen Kaisha, Tokyo
24 China Merchant Nav. Co., Hong Kong

B *How to dress a ship Dressing a ship means that national ensigns shall be displayed from the flagstaff and from each masthead. When full dressing a ship, a rainbow of signal flags and pennants is also displayed. The order of flags in the U.S. Navy is shown above. In the Royal British Navy the order shall be:*

1 Fore-down. Beginning at jack staff: E. Q, Desig, G, p3, Z, Negat, W, p9, 7, p4, R, p8, P, p4, i, p1, T, p7, 6, Corpen, 8, p2, X, Preparative, H, Code, 5, Starboard, X, pØ, F, Church pennant, Division, Form, O, Sub Division.
2 Main down. Beginning at Ensign Staff: 3, L, p2, 4, p7, X,

Church pennant, Ø, Interrogative, B, pØ, V, p4, K, pQ, N, Code, J, Form, R, Turn, M, Corpen, P, p7, 3, p3, 2, Desig, 5, p8, 9, Speed Flag.
3 Fore to Main: Station, Y, Third Substitute, U, First Substitute, D, Fourth Substitute, 3, Emergency, 1, Third Substitute, L, Emergency, 7, Second Substitute, Squadron, First Substitute, C.

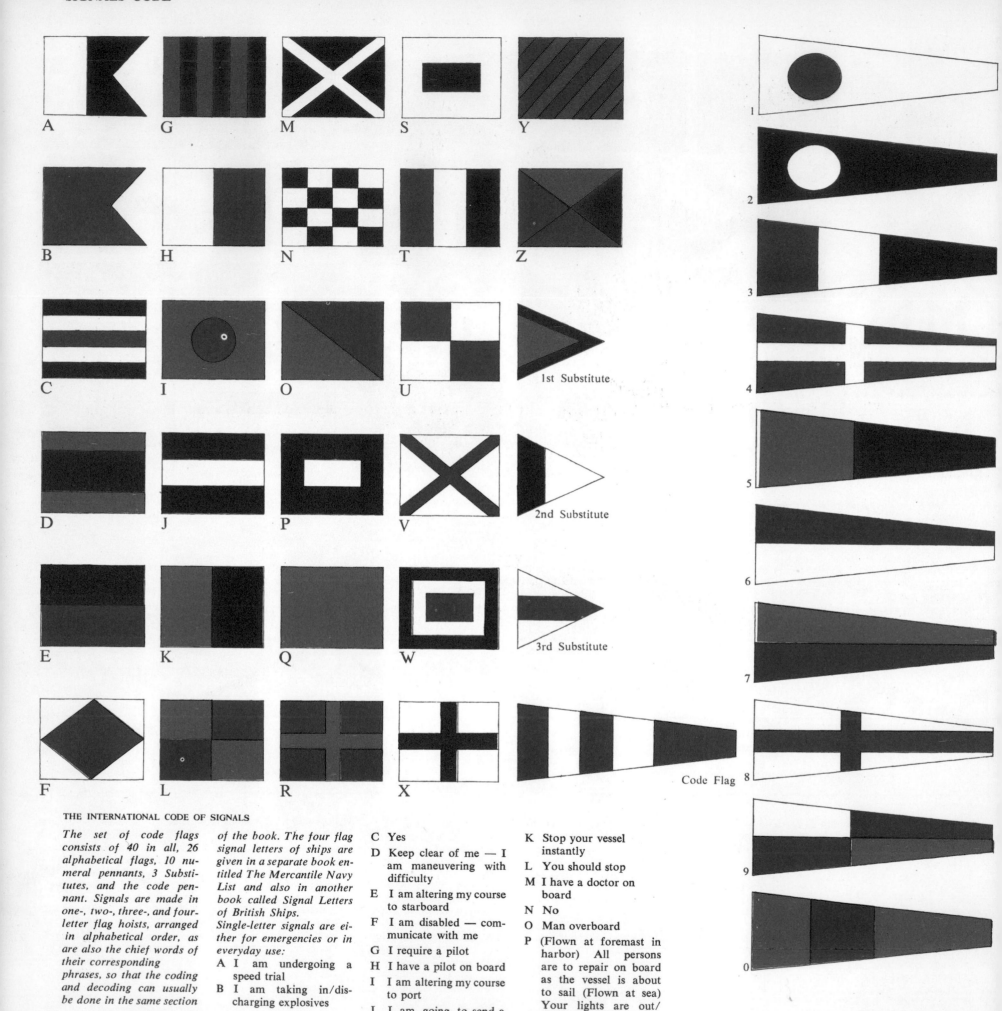

A

G

M

S

Y

B

H

N

T

Z

C

I

O

U

1st Substitute

D

J

P

V

2nd Substitute

E

K

Q

W

3rd Substitute

F

L

R

X

Code Flag

1

2

3

4

5

6

7

8

9

0

THE INTERNATIONAL CODE OF SIGNALS

The set of code flags consists of 40 in all, 26 alphabetical flags, 10 numeral pennants, 3 Substitutes, and the code pennant. Signals are made in one-, two-, three-, and four-letter flag hoists, arranged in alphabetical order, as are also the chief words of their corresponding phrases, so that the coding and decoding can usually be done in the same section of the book. The four flag signal letters of ships are given in a separate book entitled The Mercantile Navy List and also in another book called Signal Letters of British Ships.

Single-letter signals are either for emergencies or in everyday use:

A I am undergoing a speed trial

B I am taking in/discharging explosives

C Yes

D Keep clear of me — I am maneuvering with difficulty

E I am altering my course to starboard

F I am disabled — communicate with me

G I require a pilot

H I have a pilot on board

I I am altering my course to port

J I am going to send a message by semaphore

K Stop your vessel instantly

L You should stop

M I have a doctor on board

N No

O Man overboard

P (Flown at foremast in harbor) All persons are to repair on board as the vessel is about to sail (Flown at sea) Your lights are out/ burning badly

Continued

Continued

Q My vessel is healthy—I request a free pratique

R The way is off my ship you may feel your way past me

S My engines are going full speed astern

T Don't pass ahead of me

U You are standing into danger

V I require assistance

W I require medical assistance

X Stop carrying out your intentions and watch for my signals

Y I am carrying mail

Z (To be used to address shore stations)

1—0 Numeral pennants

The use of the Substitutes is described in the following section

A *The international signal code*
Selection of two-letter signals

1 AM — Accident has occurred; I require a doctor

2 NC — I am in distress and require immediate assistance

3 SC — What is the name of your vessel?

A selection of three-letter signals

4 ECE — What course are you steering? (When 1st flag is to be repeated, it is indicated by the 1st Substitute)

5 PYU — Good voyage!

Example of a four-letter signal

6 AJJO — Liverpool (When the 2nd flag is to be repeated, it is marked by the 2nd Substitute)

B *Earlier signal systems During a few decades in the middle of the 19th century. Marryat's code was in use before the Commercial Code became universal. The number in Marryat's Code of the Swedish three-masted ship Indiaman of Gävle, 1856, is shown above the ship.*

CORDAGE

A *Cable-laid rope*
1 Cable, laid up left-
   handed
2 Hawser, laid up right-
   handed
3 Strands
4 Yarn
5 Fiber

B *Direction of lay*
   In the rope trade the
   directions of the lay are
   described as Z-twist and
   S-twist, in accordance
   with the figure they
   make. Z-twist is also
   called right-hand lay
   and S-twist is called
   left-hand lay.

C *Z-laid, hawser laid,*
   right-handed rope is
   the most used
1 Z-spun yarn
2 S-twisted strand
3 Z-laid rope

D *S-laid, hawser laid, left-*
   handed rope is rather
   uncommon
1 S-spun yarn
2 Z-twisted strand
3 S-laid rope

WIRES

A *Regular lay, right lay steel wire rope*
1 Left-handed twisted strand
2 Heart of hemp
3 Steel wires
4 Hemp or jute core

B *Standard hoisting wire rope, 6×19+1*
1 Strand of 19 steel wires
2 Heart of hemp

C *Standing rigging wire rope, 6×7+1*
1 Strand of 7 steel wires
2 Heart of hemp

D *Hemp-clad wire rope, 6×(3+4)+1*
1 Wire rope
2 Hemp string
3 Jute core
4 Heart of hemp

E *Running wire rope, 6×12+7*
1 Wire
2 Jute core
3 Heart of hemp

F *Mooring line and hawser, 6×24+7*
1 Steel wire
2 Jute core
3 Heart of hemp

G *Mooring line and hawser, 6×30+7*
1 Steel wire
2 Jute core
3 Heart of hemp

H *Tiller wire rope, 6×37+1*
1 Galvanized steel or bronze wire strand
2 Heart of hemp

I *Tiller wire rope, 6×61+1*
1 Strand (like H)
2 Heart of hemp

J *Open wire-end socket*
1 Wire rope
2 Socket
3 End spread and soldered
4 Bolt with cotter pin

K *Temporary wire rope eye*
1 Wire rope
2 Wire rope bulldog grips
3 Thimble
4 Whipping

KNOTS AND WHIPPINGS

A Overhand knot
B Figure of eight knot,
   Flemish knot
C Square knot, reef knot
D Sheet bend

E Double sheet bend,
   variation
F Bowline
G Bowline on the bight

J Fisherman's bend
K Rolling hitch
L Timber hitch
M Slippery hitch
N Blackwall hitch
I Two half-hitches

O Sheepshank
P Palm and needle
   whipping
Q Common whipping

H Clove hitch

SPLICES

When splicing cordage the strands are tucked against the lay. Each strand is taken over the strand on its left and then under the next one.

A *Short splice, ropes put together before beginning to splice*

B *Long splice*

1 The ropes laid up before beginning to splice

2 Way of knotting the strands

3 Way of tucking the strands

C *Eye splice*

1 Way of placing the strand before commencing the splice

2 Way of tucking the two first strands

D *Eye splice on a wire rope, one tuck made on each strand.*

When splicing wire rope each strand is generally tucked around the same strand all the time, in the same direction, as the single wires are laid.

Columbus' stately ship can no longer serve as the introductory note for the up-to-date chapter on propulsion. Instead, a rough print of the cylinder top in a diesel motor has been used.

PROPULSION

BY TAGE BLUM

The first primitive craft, hollowed-out tree trunks or skin-covered boats built on light frames, were propelled by a paddle which was held with both hands and had no support by the gunwale. If there were many paddles on each side a considerable speed could undoubtedly be obtained. Even quite large ships have been paddled, which is apparent from many Egyptian reproductions. The "Hjortspring boat" in the National Museum in Copenhagen is a good example of a ship which had been built for propulsion by paddles. The invention of the oar with a fixed support on the gunwale was a very great advancement. The "Nydam boat" (Gottorp Castle) was an effective and fast "rowing ship" of slender shape and with twenty-eight oars. In Scandinavia the sail came into use early, and even though the Norsemen's Viking ships and longships were very easily rowed, sail was always used when making long voyages.

It was different in the Mediterranean, where the rowing vessel had a unique development. Here, they were not content with one line of oars or one man to an oar, but built vessels with two, three, and possibly more tiers of oars banked over each other. Probably the largest vessels employed several men to an oar. They were named biremes, triremes, quadriremes, quinquiremes, and so on even to one huge "40." Of these, the trireme was the best (170 oarsmen, maximum speed 8—9 knots). To give some idea of its efficiency, it was not until the time of Napoleon III that there was a faster postal service by steamship over the Mediterranean than that which the triremes maintained during Roman times. A factor should, however, be pointed out: while it was an honor to row an oar in a Viking ship, it was the slaves who rowed the Mediterranean galleys.

The idea of using paddle wheels appeared comparatively early. Appius Claudius is said to have experimented with hand-driven paddle wheels as early as the year 263 B.C. During the course of time, the idea appeared again and "walking drivers" by horses and oxen were tried. About the year 1200 mention is made of Chinese naval battles, where the warships were driven by slaves at capstans. As far as pure muscle power was concerned, the oar was undoubtedly the most effective means of propulsion. From the Middle Ages we have several illustrations of paddle-wheel ships, and in 1543 we hear of Blasco Garay's ship, which was tested in the harbor of Barcelona. But here also the paddle wheel was activated by man-power. A stronger source of propulsion was needed before mechanically driven vessels would have any practical use. Steam became the source of power that solved the problem. The name of James Watt will always be associated with the first practically applicable steam engine, where the movement of the piston was changed into a rotary motion. Watt was an instrument maker and was born in 1736. It cannot be said that he invented the steam engine, as Thomas Newcomen's atmospheric engine was already in existence, but Watt improved Newcomen's engine. It had been a clumsy device; now it was a really usable engine which could be used where a rotating shaft was required. Watt invented the condenser

and made an engine where the piston was operated by the steam pressure and not, as in Newcomen's engine, where the steam was only used to lift the piston while the atmospheric pressure above it pushed it down. Hence the name "atmospheric engine."

Now the steam engine began to be used in ships. The first name in this connection was Denis Papin, the inventor of "Papin's Pot." In the year 1707 Papin is said to have sailed down the Fulda river in a steamboat from Kassel to the Weser. Here, his boat was destroyed by the boatmen who had a monopoly of navigation on the Weser. It is doubtful if this boat was anything other than a hand-powered paddle boat. In the year 1736 the Englishman Jonathan Hull obtained a patent on a steam tugboat, but there is doubt if it ever came into being. In 1776 the Marquis Claude de Jouffroy built a steamboat in which the engine drove paddle feet. In 1783 he built a larger, paddle-wheel boat, which forced the current on the Saône river as witnessed by many spectators. In 1788—1789 the Scotsman William Symington built two less successful steamboats; all of these experiments, however, were of no significance.

About the same time, in 1785, in America, the clockmakers, John Fitch and Henry Voigt, built a steam engine in a boat which had twelve oars. This experiment was successful, and with his third boat Fitch carried on a regular passenger service on the Delaware river between Philadelphia and Trenton, a distance of thirty miles. Fitch, however, never received any recognition. It was Robert Fulton who succeeded commercially and reaped riches and fame. Originally he was an artist, but with technical interests. About this time, in 1801, William Symington built the steam tugboat, *Charlotte Dundas,* which in many ways was before its time. Its engine differed from others by having a horizontal cylinder, with the piston rod, crosshead, guides, and connecting rod acting directly on the crankshaft. It was direct-acting as compared with the beam engine. The paddle wheel was placed in the stern and was fitted with wheel rims. The helm was situated on the foredeck. Fulton studied this boat, and in 1802 built a steamboat in France. The machinery was from Boulton and Watt. At a trial on the Seine he succeeded in winning the confidence of the American Ambassador in Paris, Robert Livingston, and in 1806 he returned to America. Here, he built the paddle steamer *Clermont,* with an engine from Boulton and Watt, and in 1807 he made his historic and successful voyage up the Hudson river. Even if Fulton was not the inventor of the steamship, it was he who made the first steamship which had any practical value. The *Clermont* will always be considered a milestone in the development of the steamship. In spite of its successful voyages in 1802 it was not the *Charlotte Dundas* that opened a new era. Instead, it was forbidden the use of the Clyde canal for fear it would damage its banks. Henceforth, all steamship traffic in Great Britain was stopped until years later. In America, under more favorable circumstances, development of steamships on the big rivers was rapid. Five years after the *Clermont's*

journey there were fifty steamships in regular service. The high speeds attained by these paddle steamers are rather surprising: for example, the fastest ship at that time, the *Daniel Drew* of 1860, was able to maintain an average speed of 22 knots. However, these were large ships! For instance, the *New World* was 380 feet long, had a paddle wheel of 46 feet in diameter, and had no less than 680 berths.

Not until 1812 did the building of steamships begin in Europe. This was when Henry Bell launched the *Comet,* a ship with a length of 40 feet and a beam of 10½ feet. The engine was a single cylinder unit of 3—4 horsepower and the speed was only 4—5 knots. It differed from other paddle steamers by having two wheels on each side. The whole engine installation was much more primitive than that of the *Charlotte Dundas,* but, in spite of this, the *Comet* became the model for practical steamship service in England.

At first, steamships were looked upon as only suitable for river and coastal traffic; possibilities for development were a lot greater in America with its large waterways. It is therefore notable that it was an American steamship that first crossed the Atlantic. On May 26, 1819, the *Savannah* left Savannah, Georgia, and arrived at Liverpool twenty-five days later. *Savannah* was a full-rigged ship, fitted with a 90 horsepower engine that drove the wheel shaft directly. The paddle wheels were sixteen feet in diameter and were fitted with chains instead of wheel rims, so that the paddle wheels could be folded up when the sails were in use. From the logbook it can be seen that the steam engine was used for eighteen days of the voyage, while only the sails were used during the remaining seven days. The *Savannah's* dimensions were: length 100 feet; beam 27 feet 9 inches; draft 14 feet. The vessel held seventy-five tons of coal and three-thousand cubic feet of wood bunkers.

The ships mentioned up to now, with the exception of the *Charlotte Dundas* and the *Savannah,* were all fitted with beam engines on which the piston rod was joined to one end of a center pivoted rocker beam and the crankshaft to the other end. There were many variations of the beam engine: engines with the beam above, and engines with the beam below; also the "grasshopper engines," with the beam pivoted at one end. In Europe a low-location beam was mostly used, as this gave a low center of gravity. Paddle wheels, in the beginning, had fixed paddles, but these were inefficient. Soon, movable paddles came into being. These paddles could, by means of a series of rods, operated by a cam, stand almost vertical during the whole time they were under water (Morgan's patent paddle wheel).

As early as about 1770 the French scientist, Daniel Bernoulli, had suggested the propeller as a means of propulsion. There were both corkscrew and windmill types. In 1836 the Englishman, E. P. Smith, made a propeller that resembled a corkscrew, while the Swede, John Ericsson, experimented with a propeller that resembled the sails of a windmill. Smith's propeller had a pitch of $1\frac{1}{2}$—3 turns to start with, but during one of the test runs part of it was knocked off and it was then found that it was much more effective. John Ericsson, who was born in 1803 and died in 1889, built a successful propeller-driven boat, the *Francis B. Ogden,* which was demonstrated on the Thames in 1837. His idea, however, was not popularly received, so he left for America where he quickly met with great success. Among the early propeller ships, Samuel Owen's *The Witch of Stockholm,* 1816, should be mentioned.

The engines used in paddle steamers were much too slow to drive propellers, and attempts were made to increase the speed by means of gears or chain transmission (*S/S Great Britain,* 1839), but these gearings did not solve the problem. Although the propeller had many advantages over the paddle wheel it was a long time before the propeller became a real success. The majority preferred the paddle steamer for passenger traffic and were responsible for the building of the last of the large paddle steamers: *Persia* (1855) and *Scotia* (1862). Especially interesting was the tug of war carried out by the British Navy between H.M.S. *Rattler* (propeller) and the equally large and powerful H.M.S. *Alecto* (paddle wheel). It was a great victory for the propeller.

A unique change was represented by the gigantic ship *Great Eastern* (trials, 1859), which was equipped with both propeller (24 feet in diameter) and paddle wheels (56 feet in diameter, each weighing 92 tons). Commercially, the ship was a failure, but even so, it will always be looked upon as a milestone in the history of shipbuilding.

The first boilers were very primitive, with an external firebox and often with large flat surfaces. These pot-boilers could not stand high pressures. They were then developed into boilers with internal fireboxes, and then into fire tube boilers with combustion chambers and several fire tubes. This increased the heating area and used the fuel more effectively. Fire tube boilers (the Scotch boilers) became the commonest type in merchant ships about 1900 and later. Development continued with water tube boilers, where the water (as opposed to the fire tube boilers) is contained inside the tubes and the furnace and combustion gases are outside. Water tube boilers contain less water than fire tube boilers. Steam can be raised much more quickly with a water tube boiler than with a Scotch boiler. They became even more economical with the introduction of the super-heater, artificial draft created by fans, preheating of the water, and so on. The engine went through a comparable development, to direct-acting vertical steam engines with the crankshaft placed under the cylinders. The expansion of steam became more efficient with the use of a three-cylinder engine with high, medium, and low pressure cylinders. The triple-expansion engine became the most usual type in the merchant navy.

A really powerful engine had been developed in the shape of the reciprocating steam engine, but it was, however, of rather complicated construction. It was, therefore, obvious that an engine where the energy was directly transformed into rotation had to be built.

As far back as two-thousand years ago, Hero of Alexandria described such a machine. It was the famous Hero steam ball, which was a complete reactive turbine. In 1629 the Italian, Johann Branca, described a machine where a jet of steam drove a bladed wheel. This was also a turbine, an active turbine. Both were only curiosities, and it was to take centuries before the first usable turbine was designed by the Swede, de Laval.

De Laval's turbine was an active one where the expansion of the steam took place in a stationary turbine casing. This is called an equal pressure turbine because the steam acts directly on the rotor. With high rotor speed, about 30,000 r.p.m., and consequently, great centrifugal force, it was difficult to transmit the power to slower rotating shafts. It was necessary to expand steam pressure through several stages. This brings us to multi-stage turbines and such inventors as Zoelly, Curtis, and Parsons, who used several rotors on the same shaft but separated them with stationary guide blade rings.

The most important figure in the development of the steam turbine as a marine-power plant was Sir Charles Parsons, who built the first turbine-powered ship, the steam yacht *Turbinia,* powered by a 2,000 s.h.p. turbine, which drove a propeller at approximately 1,800 r.p.m. The first trials were a disappointment: a speed of $19\frac{3}{4}$ knots at 1,780 r.p.m. The trouble was that at such high revolutions cavitation occurred at the propeller, a problem of which little was then known.

In 1893, the *Turbinia's* power plant was rebuilt with three turbines, each driving its own shaft, and with a total of nine propellers. With this change came success: a maximum speed of up to 34 knots — a rather incredible speed at that time. The Admiralty, however, showed no interest in it. This led to Parsons' historical demonstration, in 1897, at the naval review at Spithead. Parsons sailed at a speed of over 30 knots past the warships at anchor. A naval vessel was sent out to stop the unwelcome visitor, but the speed of the *Turbinia* only made the naval ship look ridiculous. This demonstration resulted in an order for the first turbine-powered destroyer, H.M.S. *Viper.* The steam turbine had many advantages compared with the reciprocating engine, such as no vibration and less space required for the same amount of power. Nevertheless, while direct drive was used, trouble with propeller cavitation was encountered. This trouble was not overcome until gears, which could transmit high power, were developed. Naval ships, as well as large passenger ships, where vibration had to be kept to a minimum quickly changed to steam turbines.

Just before the steam engine and the steam turbine reached the peak of their development a new source of power appeared: the diesel engine. Even the best steam plant is still an external combustion engine in which the fuel's energy is converted into dynamic energy through an intermediate means. If an engine could be made where the actual combustion took place inside the cylinder, greater power for the same amount of fuel could be attained. It was this which Rudolf Diesel (1858—1913) did when he invented the engine which now bears his name all over the world. Diesel soon decided to make such an internal combustion engine. In 1893 he described in a treatise the theory and construction of an internal combustion engine, and this put him in contact with the two well-known concerns of Krupp and M.A.N., which then did everything to complete the task. The first usable diesel engine was completed in 1897. Its main principle was the ignition of the fuel itself in the cylinder when highly compressed with air. The temperature rose to about 800°C. During combustion (not explosion), the piston was pushed down the cylinder. The diesel engine used about thirty-five per cent of the energy in the fuel, while the steam engine used only fifteen per cent.

The person who was of the greatest importance in the development of the marine diesel engine was, however, the Dane, Ivar Knudsen, the Director of A/S Burmeister & Wain, who, in 1897, succeeded in producing a directly

reversible engine. On February 12, 1912, the first ocean-going motor ship the *Selandia,* sailed on its maiden voyage, introducing a new era in international shipping. Here, the manager of B. & W.'s diesel engine design department, Dr. H. H. Blacke, must be mentioned as another important man in the development of the diesel engine. Blacke was awarded the James Watt medal, a very rare honor for non-Englishmen.

Development progressed from the *Selandia's* four-stroke engine, with compressed air for the injection of fuel oil, to double-acting four-stroke engines (in the first *Gripsholm*), two-stroke engines, double-acting two-stroke engines with fuel pressure feed pump to the modern two-stroke engine with exhaust-driven superchargers, which is the most popular engine today. The large diesel engine was a source of power which could be competitive with the steam turbine, even when the great power needed for supertankers and fast cargo liners was considered.

The diesel engine, even so, is a piston engine, with many heavy reciprocating mechanical parts. The need was therefore obvious for a combustion turbine, where the energy from the combustion gases was directly transferred to a gas turbine. The greatest difficulty was in overcoming the very high temperatures. Materials have now been discovered which can stand up to such great heat, and today there are ships powered by gas turbines with combustion chambers, heat exchangers, superchargers etc., as well as gas turbines in connection with free piston engines.

Ever since the atom was successfully split, scientists have been searching for ways to put this mighty power to practical use. In the reactors, where the fission of atoms takes place, heat is produced; this is used to produce steam, which is then used in steam turbines. It may seem rather primitive, generally speaking, to use a reactor instead of fuel for a boiler. For the present, however, it would seem to be the only method of utilizing this tremendous energy. The difference between combustion and fission is that when one unit of nuclear fuel (uranium or similar material) is split, two million times as much heat is produced as when one unit of fuel oil is burned.

The reactor in which actual fission takes place is a very strong steel container. By means of a coolant, the heat of nuclear fission is transferred to a heat exchanger in which pipes filled with water receive the heat and produce steam. The steam is used to drive a turbine and then returns to the heat exchanger via a condenser. This is, roughly speaking, the principle used in a ship's reactor. To be able to use nuclear power safely it is necessary to have an effective screen against radiation. This screening is always very heavy (in the N/S *Savannah* about 1,900 tons) and even though the nuclear fuel is light, it is very expensive (about $16,000 per kg.). A nuclear installation cannot, therefore, compete with a diesel or turbine installation because of its prohibitive cost, in spite of great operational range.

With the first American nuclear submarine, the *Nautilus,* and the first nuclear-powered merchant vessel, the *Savannah,* we stand on the threshold of an enormous development of one of the greatest sources of power in the history of mankind.

A 1

A 2

B

C

D

E 2

E 1

F

OARS

A **Old galley oar**
Because of their size, these oars were always built with the blade bolted to the shaft. They had handles so that four men could pull each oar.

B **Old Indian paddle**
C **Old Egyptian paddle**
D **Eskimo paddle**

E **Greek warship from 500 B.C.**
1 Drawing from a vase painting
2 Sketch showing the position of oars in a bireme, that is, a boat with two banks of oars on each side

F **Peruvian raft of balsa wood, with sail and paddles (from Benzoni)**

OARS

A *Oars from a book on shipbuilding by Rålamb, A.C., 1691*

1, 2 The longest oar that can be pulled by one man should not exceed 16½ feet. An oar should never be more than three times the beam of the boat.

3 A handy oar for one man is 14 feet in length

4 When sculling, the oars should not be more than 9 feet and not more than 1½ times the beam of the boat

5 A pulling boat, 20 feet long, pulling ten oars

B *Medieval boat with paddle wheels*

C *Modern competition rowing*

1 Four oars with outriggers, no coxswain

2 Position of oarsman when pulling

3 The path of the oar blade during a stroke

D *The oar*

1 Grip

2 Loom

3 Leather-covered seat

4 Shaft

5 Blade

6 Copper-banded tip

PADDLE WHEEL AND OLD PADDLE ENGINES

A *Symington's direct-drive*   5 Paddle wheel
   steamship engine, 1802   6 Steampipe
1 Boiler   7 Safety valve
2 Cylinder   8 Condenser
3 Piston rod   9 Pump
4 Connecting rod   10 Smoke box
                                  11 Funnel

B *Geared steam engine of*   4 Balance
   the Clermont by   5 Bearing
   Fulton, 1807   6 Connecting rod
1 Cylinder   7 Flywheel
2 Piston rod   8 Gear
3 Condenser   9 Paddle wheel

C *Paddle wheel*   6 Paddle
1 Paddle shaft   7 Wrist pin
2 Hub   8 Limbs
3 Spoke   9 Drag link
4 Inner rim   10 Eccentric strap
5 Outer rim   11 King rod

PADDLE WHEEL ENGINE AND OLD PROPELLERS

A	*Propeller development*		4 Connecting rod	10 Oil cup	16 Tail rod	21 Double-bar link
1	1785		5 Eccentric	11 HP-cylinder steam inlet	17 LP-cylinder	22 Cooling water, inlet
2	1800	B *Triple-expansion*	6 Eccentric strap	12 LP-cylinder exhaust	18 LP-cylinder steam	23 Cooling water, outlet
3	1812	*paddle wheel engine*	7 Oil cup	pipe	inlet	24 Condenser
4	1840	1 Foundation	8 Connecting rod	13 Reversing lever	19 Valve-spindle guide	25 Pipe to vacuum pump
5	1860	2 Crank shaft	9 Eccentric rods	14 Throttle valve wheel	20 Link operating bar	26 Tank top plating
		3 Turning gear		15 Throttle valve wheel		27 Bottom plating
						28 Plate floor

VARIOUS TYPES OF OLDER BOILERS

A *Rectangular or box boiler*
1 Uptake
2 Steam space
3 Water level
4 Boiler tubes
5 Combustion chamber
6 Furnace
7 Ash pit
8 Furnace bars
9 Furnace bridge

B *Vertical donkey boiler*
1 Donkey funnel
2 Crown of donkey boiler
3 Manhole door
4 Sludge hole doors
5 Furnace door
6 Safety valve
7 Steam pipe
8 Gauge glass
9 Feed pipe

C *Cylindrical boiler (Scotch type)*
1 Dome
2 Uptake and smoke box
3 Furnaces
4 Shell of boiler

D *Oval donkey boiler*
1 Uptake and smoke box
2 Smoke box door
3 Furnace front
4 Furnace door
5 Furnace and ash pit
6 Back plate
7 Front plate
8 Back tube-plate
9 Boiler bearer

E *Water tube donkey boiler*
1 Funnel
2 Water tubes

F *Double-ended boiler*
1 Steam space
2 Water level
3 Boiler stays
4 Boiler tubes
5 Combustion chamber
6 Furnaces
7 Ash pits

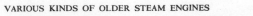

VARIOUS KINDS OF OLDER STEAM ENGINES

A *Side lever engine*
B *Overhead beam engine*

C *Grasshopper engine*
D *Inverted vertical reciprocating compound engine*

E *Steeple engine*
F *Oscillating engine*

G *Diagonal engine*
H *Horizontal (trunk) engine*

ENGINE AND BOILER, 1880

A *Midship section of a steamer, showing boiler room*
1 Floor
2 Water ballast in double bottom
3 Brackets
4 Boiler bearers
5 Ash pits
6 Front tube plates
7 Smoke box, uptake
8 Smoke box doors
9 Side coal bunkers
10 Bunker stays
11 Safety valves
12 Funnel
13 Funnel cape
14 Air casing of funnel
15 Fidley
16 Fidley gratings
17 Bridge deck beam
18 Alley-way, in bridge-house
19 Officer's room
20 Upper deck beam
21 Lower deck beam
22 Flat plate keel
23 Garboard strakes
24 Bottom plating
25 Bilge keel
26 Side plating
27 Sheer strake
28 Side plating of bridge
29 Sheer strake of bridge
30 Fidley top

B *Triple-expansion engine*
1 Bedplate
2 Crank shaft
3 Main bearings
4 Cylinder columns
5 Hand rail
6 Reversing wheel
7 Weigh shaft
8 Weigh shaft arms
9 High-pressure connecting rod
10 Intermediate-pressure connecting rod
11 Low-pressure connecting rod
12 Condenser
13 Condenser head
14 Circulating-pump discharge pipe
15 Exhaust pipe
16, 17, 18 Eccentric rods
19, 21, 23 Valve spindles
20, 22, 24 Valve spindle guides
25, 27, 29 Piston rods
26, 28, 30 Piston rod crossheads
31 Pump levers
32 Pump links
33 High-pressure cylinder
34, 36, 38 Cylinder covers
35 Intermediate cylinder
37 Low-pressure cylinder
39, 40, 41 Valve casings
42, 43, 44 Balance cylinders
45, 46, 47 Escape valves
48 Starting valve
49 Starting valve pipe
50 Throttle
51, 52, 53 Tail rods
54 Stuffing boxes

OLD STEAM ENGINE AND ANCILLARY DETAILS, FROM AN OLD DRAWING

A *Propeller tail shaft*	12 Stern post	10 Slide valve	22 Cylinder column	D *Propeller*	F *Piston, seen from above*
1 Coupling flange	13 Stern tube nut	11 Slide valve casing	23 Reversing wheel	15 Propeller hub	2 Piston
2 Sleeve	14 Guard ring	12 Slide valve casing door	24 Eccentric rods	18 Propeller blades	31 Junk ring
3 Keyway	B *Piston steam engine*	13 Slide valve rod	25 Eccentric straps		33 Junk ring bolts
4 Tail end	1 Cylinder	14 Valve rod guide	26 Main bearing	E *Piston*	34 Guard ring tail
5 Stuffing-box gland	2 Piston	15 Piston rod crosshead	27 Crank web	2 Piston	G *Propeller shaft, end*
6 Stern tube flange	3 Piston rod	16 Crosshead guide	28 Crank shaft	3 Piston rod	*view*
7 Stuffing-box bulkhead	4 Tail rod	17 Connecting rod	29 Condenser	4 Tail rod	10 Stern tube
8 Tunnel cock	5 Cylinder cover	18 Pump links	30 Bedplates	31 Junk ring	11 Stern tube bushing
9 Water pipe	6 Escape valve	19 Pump levers		32 Packing rings	12 Stern post
10 Stern tube	7 Stuffing box	20 Weigh shaft	C *Throttle valve*	33 Junk ring bolts	14 Guard ring
11 Stern tube bushing	8 Steam ports	21 Weigh shaft arms	35 Throttle valve		
	9 Steam ports		36 Throttle valve spindle		
			37 Steam pipe		

MODERN BOILER AND ENGINE

A *Quadruple steam engine, starboard engine of a twin-screw steamer*

1 HP-cylinder
2 Piston rod
3 Cylinder cover
4 Steam line to intermediate reheater
5 Piston valve
6 1st IP-cylinder
7 Piston
8 Safety valve
9 2nd IP-cylinder
10 Piston
11 Steam line from turbocompressor
12 LP-cylinder
13 Piston
14 Extraction steam ports
15 Piston rod box
16 Piston rod
17 Crosshead
18 Condenser head
19 Turning gear
20 Crank shaft
21 Bedplate
22 Main bearing
23 LP-connecting rod
24 Condenser
25 Eccentric rods
26 Double-bar link
27 Eccentrics and straps
28 2nd IP-connecting rod
29 Condenser head
30 1st IP-connecting rod
31 Eccentrics and straps
32 Eccentric rods
33 Crank web
34 Crank pin
35 HP-connecting rod
36 Crosshead guide plates
37 Valve spindle
38 Stuffing-box
39 Crosshead
40 Engine frame

B *Water-tube boiler, header boiler*

1 Steam outlet
2 Dry pipe
3 Steam drum
4 Steam space
5 Feed-water pipe
6 Manhole
7 Water level
8 Steam collecting baffle
9 1st tube bank
10 2nd tube bank
11 Hand hole plates
12 Boiler casing
13 Rear header
14 Mud drum
15 Furnace bridge
16 Furnace-bars (-grate)
17 Ash pit
18 Ash pit door
19 Furnace
20 Furnace door
21 Locking handle
22 Front header
23 Return tubes
24 Cross box
25 Economizer
26 Uptake

ENGINE ROOM TELEGRAPH

Orders are transmitted from the bridge to the engine room by means of a wire and chain telegraph on the bridge and another in the engine room, so that orders from the bridge can be repeated in the engine room for confirmation. In a twin-screw ship there is one telegraph for each engine.

A *Wire-operated telegraph*
1 When the lever is moved to, say, STOP on the bridge telegraph the pointer on the engine room telegraph moves to that same position. The engineer then replies by moving the lever of his telegraph to STOP. By so doing, the correponding pointer on the bridge (2) moves to STOP, thus indicating that the order has been understood and is being executed.

B *Electrical telegraph for a twin-screw vessel, worked on this same principle but by electricity*

C *Control panel of the engine room, with the engine room telegraph shown on the left on the panel*

NUCLEAR POWER

A *Principle of atomic fission*	5 Moderator	B *Nuclear ship plant*	6· Boiler	C *Nuclear ship*	6 Hold no. 3
1 Uranium atomic nucleus	6 Low speed neutrons	1 Nuclear fuel elements	7 Steam turbine	1 Reactor	7 Hold no. 4
2 Nucleus fragments	7 Control rod	2 Heated fluid	8 Gear	2 Propulsion turbines	8 Hold no. 5
3 High speed neutrons	8 Absorbed neutron	3 Control rods	9 Driving shaft	3 Superstructure	9 Hold no. 6
4 Heat energy	9 Low speed neutron on its way to split atomic nucleus	4 Heat exchanger	10 Condenser	4 Hold no. 1	10 Hold no. 7
		5 Lead radiation shielding	11 Feedwater pump	5 Hold no. 2	

EARLY STEAMERS

1 *Pyroscape*, built by Marquis Claude de Jouffrouy d' Abbans, 1783.

2 *Charlotte Dundas*, built for the Forth and Clyde Canal in 1802.

3 *Clermont*, built in 1807 by Robert Fulton for the Hudson River between New York and Albany.

4 *Comet*, built in 1812 by James Watt for service on the Clyde.

5 *The Witch of Stockholm*, built by Samuel Owens in 1816.

6 *Savannah*, built in 1818. As the first steamship she crossed the Atlantic in 1819. It is worth mentioning that she used her engine for only short periods during the voyage.

7 *Great Western*, built in 1838. First steamer in transatlantic service.

8 *Rob. F. Stockton*, built in 1839. The first iron hulled vessel to cross the Atlantic.

9 *Hamburger Paquet*, built in Gothenburg in 1858.

10 *Great Eastern*, built in 1858, length 692 ft., displacement 27,400 tons, speed 15 knots, crew 400, passengers 4,000. In her time she was the biggest ship in the world, and was not surpassed in size until 1899.

EARLY STEAMERS

11 Side-wheeler *Natchez.*
Until 1870 the fastest
boat on the Mississippi
River.

12 A paddle steamer from
1873.

13 The passenger steamer,
Odin, built in 1875.

14 The tank steamer
Gluckauf, built in 1886
in Great Britain for
German owners. The
first modern tanker.

15 The passenger vessel,
Deutschland, built in
1900, length about 670
ft., speed 24 knots.

16 Turret deck steamer
from 1907.

17 *Mauretania,* 1913,
33,000 gross tons regis-
ter, speed 25.8 knots,
length about 760 ft.

SOME MODERN SHIPS

18 British collier, a ship
    that chiefly carries
    North Country coal to
    London
19 *Selandia*. The first
    ocean-going cargo die-
    sel motorship in the
    world, built in Den-
    mark in 1911

20 *Amerikaland*.
    Swedish ore-carrying
    vessel, built in 1925 for
    service between South
    and North America,
    22,800 tons dwt.
21 Motor ship, 1930

22 U.S. Liberty standard
    vessel, displacement
    14,000 tons

SOME MODERN SHIPS

23 U.S. C-2 standard vessel, displacement, 13,900 tons dwt., capacity 9,000 tons

24 A coastal tanker of about 800 tons dwt.

25 A small Dutch motor coaster

26 Passenger ship used on short sea routes, for instance, the cross Channel service, about 3,000 gross tons

27 Ore tanker, 1950 Midship section of same ship
a. Oil tanks
b. Hold for ore

SOME MODERN SHIPS

28 Fruit carrier of about
    4,000 gross tons, 15
    knots
29 Turbine passenger ves-
    sel, 40,000 gross tons

30 Motor tanker of 40,000
    tons dwt, speed 16½
    knots. (At the time she
    was built, 1958, she was
    the largest motor tan-
    ker in the world)

31 Modern cargo liner of
    9,600 tons dwt, and
    7,200 gross tons,
    accommodations for
    12 passengers

SOME MODERN SHIPS

32 Modern train and car ferry in service between Denmark and Germany, 5,500 gross tons

33 The largest ship hitherto built, 1962, the Japanese mammoth tanker, *Nissho Maru*, 132,000 tons dwt

34 Modern passenger liner, *France*, gross tonnage 66,000, length 1,035 ft., breadth 110 ft., 2,044 passengers, service speed 30 knots

35 The nuclear-powered cargo vessel *Savannah*, displacement 22,000 tons, accommodations for 60 passengers, speed 20½ knots

LONGITUDINAL VIEW OF A 10-CYLINDER, TURBOCHARGED 2-STROKE, CROSSHEAD, DIRECT DRIVE, PROPULSION DIESEL ENGINE

1 Fore end cylinder
2 Overhead cooling water pipe
3 Exhaust gas valve yoke
4 Encased valve springs
5 Cylinder cover
6 Cylinder lubricator
7 Fuel injection pump
8 Air receiver access
9 Cam shaft
10 Door to crosshead guide
11 Crankcase access door
12 Fore end of crankshaft

13 Crank pin bearing
14 Crank web
15 Connecting rod
16 Crosshead shoe
17 Crosshead bearing
18 Piston rod stuffing box
19 Scavenging ports
20 Cylinder liner
21 Working piston with rings
22 Fuel valve
23 Indicator valve
24 Forward turbocharger
25 Air compressor intake

26 Gas turbine outlet to boiler
27 Turbocharger by-pass pipe
28 Chain transmission stretcher
29 Chain transmission casing
30 Over-speed governor
31 Gauge board
32 Engine room telegraph
33 Master starting air valve wheel
34 Maneuvering hand-wheel

35 Telegraph reply wheel
36 Forward oil pan
37 Oil pan drain
38 Scavenging air pumps connecting arms
39 Scavenging air double-acting pumps
40 Scavenging air receiver
41 Aft turbocharger
42 Top end of valve drag links
43 Exhaust gas pipe
44 Exhaust gas valve

45 Cylinder in position for scavenging
46 Scavenging ports
47 Water cooling jacket
48 Scavenging air receiver
49 Oil cooling channels
50 Valve drag links
51 Piston rod oil cooling pipes
52 Crosshead pin
53 Cooling oil entrance
54 Telescope arm
55 Telescope pipe
56 Cooling oil drain

57 Connecting rod lubricating pipe
58 Exhaust valve cam segment
59 Cam rollers
60 Exhaust valve levers
61 Crankshaft journal and main bearing
62 Crank pin and connecting rod bearing
63 Aft oil pan
64 Oil pan drain
65 Propeller thrust bearing
66 Electric turning motor

A

B

C

D

E

Continued

9 Shelter deck (B deck)
10 Ventilation duct
11 Main deck (C deck)
12 Daily use fuel tanks
13 Lower deck (D deck)
14 Shaft tunnel
15 Propeller shaft
16 Turning gear
17 Propeller thrust bearing
18 Double bottom tanks
19 Tank top
20 Starboard main diesel engine
21 Ladder
22 Boiler
23 Auxiliary diesel engine
24 Electric generator
25 Engine room flooring

26 Platform
27 Main switchboard
28 Silencers, auxiliary engines
29 Diesel oil tanks
30 Main diesel exhaust pipe
31 Boiler exhaust pipe
32 Walking passages
33 Navigating bridge
34 Exhaust boiler
35 Tyfon
36 Boiler exhaust
37 Exhaust boiler outlet
38 Exhaust boiler by-pass and spark arrester
39 Exhaust casing entrance
40 Funnel

D *2-stroke diesel engine principle*
I Compression stroke
II Power stroke
III Scavenging
4 Scavenging air-receiver
5 Scavenging ports
6 Combustion chamber
7 Exhaust gas valve
8 Cylinder cover
9 Fuel pipe
10 Exhaust manifold
11 Valve spindle
12 Fuel valve
13 Cylinder liner
14 Piston

E *Cross section of a 2-stroke, crosshead, direct drive, propulsion diesel engine*
1 Overhead cooling-water pipe
2 Exhaust pipe
3 Starting air valve
4 Top platform
5 Exhaust receiver
6 Suction valves
7 Piston rod stuffing box
8 Bottom cooling water pipe
9 Piston cooling oil telescopic pipe
10 Piston rod
11 Scavenging air pump connecting arm
12 Lower platform (starboard side)

13 Lubricating and cooling oil main pipe
14 Connecting rod
15 Crank end bearing
16 Main-bearing lubricant pipe
17 Main lubricant pipe
18 Bedplate
19 Crank pin
20 Cast steel saddles
21 Crank case
22 Crank shaft
23 Lubricating and cooling oil return pipe
24 Exhaust valve cam segment
25 Cam roller
26 Exhaust valve lever
27 Exhaust valve pull rod
28 Crosshead bearing
29 Crosshead pin

30 Crosshead shoe
31 Crosshead guide
32 Lower platform (port side)
33 Scavenging air compression chamber
34 Scavenging air delivery valve
35 Scavenging air receiver
36 Cam shaft
37 Oil-cooled working piston
38 Fuel-injection pump
39 Fuel valve
40 Exhaust-gas valve
41 Water-cooled cylinder cover
42 Cooling water
43 Exhaust-gas valve yoke

FISHING

BY GERHARD TIMMERMANN

It is not really known when man started collecting living creatures from the sea as part of his food. Probably fish and other sea creatures were at first caught with the bare hands. This is still done in some places even today. This primitive method of catching fish is little used now even though sponges, mussels, oysters, and other boneless animals are often taken in this manner. It is quite possible that early man watched animals catching fish for food and then imitated them.

The oldest fishing equipment known has come from the early European Stone Age (20,000-8,000 B.C.) in the form of small fish spears or harpoons that were hand-thrown. Similar spears are still used today in the tropics, where they are usually driven from a blowgun instead of being thrown. In some tropical areas one can also come across natives fishing with the bow and arrow; this is an ancient fishing method. The use of guns or small cannon for shooting harpoons dates from about the middle of the 19th century.

Catching fish with bait can be traced a long way back in time, as fish hooks made of stone have been found in layers of earth dating from Europe's middle Stone Age, i.e., around 8,000-3,000 B.C. The fishing rod has been gradually developed in a large number of different forms and sizes, rods with lines having one hook, rods with lines having several hooks, etc. Long anchored or drifting lines to which numerous short lines with hooks are attached have also been used in bait fishing. Big hooks up to fifteen inches in length are used for catching large fish, while moderate-sized hooks are used for catching smaller fish. When fishing for sharks or tunny, hooks fitted with electrical stunning devices have been used for several years.

From the point of view of profit, the most important line fishing is found on the Grand Banks off Newfoundland. Here, French-Canadian, Portuguese, and, formerly, American fishermen catch cod from small boats called dories. Their daily catches are taken to a depot ship, usually a schooner or motor schooner, where the fish are preserved by salting and drying. These cod fisheries are of considerable importance to the economics of the fish-eating Catholic countries of southern Europe.

Bait is also used in setting various types of traps, where the fish is lured by the bait into a compartment from which it cannot possibly escape. Equipment of this type can be found in many different forms. Traps can be of woven or bound branches, or they can consist of nets stretched over wooden or metal frames, and so on. The oldest historical reproductions of this kind of equipment are shown on Egyptian reliefs from the 5th Dynasty, 3160-2920 B.C. In some places, traps of this kind are used without bait. These are usually permanent traps of very complicated form having long trap arms consisting of branches or wire netting. In spite of different forms of construction, the principle is always the same. A trap is placed where the fish, for hydrological reasons (tides or currents) or biological reasons (spawning season and the search for food), is compelled to travel in a certain direction. The historian, Pliny, (23-70 A.D.) described how walls were made of branches and were placed along the German coast during the ebb tide.

Fishing nets were used as early as the Stone Age, and their use is portrayed on early Egyptian reliefs from the 4th Dynasty (3430-3160 B.C.). When making nets, it is necessary to produce square or rhombic-shaped meshes, with knots that cannot slip sideways. Permanent nets can be anchored to the sea bed as floating vertical walls or be tied like sacks to posts having wooden or metal frames. There are a great number of such devices used almost entirely in coastal fishing. When setting out such nets comparatively small boats are used. In the beginning these boats were made of hollowed-out tree trunks, evidence of this is available from as early as about 6000 B.C. During the course of time, this method of boat building developed into clinker-built boats. In the Mediterranean area the raft was probably the boat's origin. This supposition is strengthened by relief pictures from Egypt dating from about 3000 B.C. In Greenland, Ireland, and Wales, where there is a shortage of wood, boats were, and still are, built of bone or wood frames and animal hides were stretched over these. Carvel-built vessels originated in the Mediterranean and, after modification in Northern Europe, were used all over the world. In some cases fishing boats were equipped with wells through which water flowed to keep the catch alive until the boat reached shore. Modern fishing boats have insulated holds in which the catch is kept on ice. Over the years there has been a great variety of fishing boats, and their appearance has differed both in hull and rig.

Drift nets are used when fishing for large shoals of fish. They have been employed since the Middle Ages. These nets hang vertically near the surface suspended from floats of cork, glass, plastic, and so on. One end of the drift net is attached to the fishing vessel. It is said that this type of net was first used by the Dutch, about 1416, for herring fishing in the North Sea. Since then, the herring has been of great importance in the food supply of middle Europe. In this kind of fishing, the Dutch, French, and Germans first used round, bilged, square-rigged boats called busses, which were later replaced by small luggers. The catch was salted down in barrels on board, which were also used to transport the fish over long distances inland. This method of preservation was not so essential in Scandinavia and England, where there are usually no great distances between the fishing grounds and the consumer; it was used mainly for fish which were to be exported. Drift nets were originally about 1,700 to 2,000 yards long, but since the introduction of steam and motor-driven vessels the length has been increased to about 5,500 yards.

Another type of net used for herring fishing is the ring net. It encloses the shoal and is then pulled together around the fish. The net usually hangs down near the sea bed. In coastal fishing the net is laid out in a semicircle from the beach, and when drawn in toward the shore, the encircled fish are caught. At sea, ring-netting is accomplished by two ships which pay out the net while steaming away from each other; they then come together again after completing a semicircle. When ring-netting with one boat, one end of the net is anchored and the boat then steams in a large circle back to the anchoring place.

The largest net of this type is a ring net which was invented in America at the beginning of the 19th century. It is now also common in Europe. This net is laid out in a circle around a previously located shoal of fish. At the lower edge of the net there is a rope line strung through rings, by which the net can be pulled together at the bottom to form a cone. Then the catch can be taken into the boat. This form of net is commonly called a purse seine.

The most important method of fishing, however, is with the trawl. As long ago as the Middle Ages fishing was done with a boom trawl, *i.e.,* a net bag held open by a boom or pole was dragged along the sea bottom. It was not, however, until the end of the 19th century that trawl fishing had been developed to the point where its economic advantages became apparent. It was the British invention of the otter board, a kind of rudder that replaced the boom, and the introduction of steam and motor trawlers during this century that proved the economic superiority of trawl fishing. Although the French first used steam trawlers, it was mainly in England and Germany that mechanically propelled trawlers were developed and improved.

To make trawling even more profitable, trawls were fitted with a second otter board at the head of the trawl, thus achieving a greater width of net opening. Trawling with two vessels is also a useful method. This kind of trawling has been in existence in the Baltic since the 16th century, to a certain extent by Spanish fisherman through the ages, and since 1940 in the North Sea.

All fish are not caught on the sea bed. For catches at shallow depths, trawls, which can be set for changing depths, have been used for some years. The trawling depth is altered by varying the speed of the ship, and also by using different lengths of trawl line.

After the Second World War deep-sea fishing was spurred by the echo sounder, which not only made it possible to measure the depth of water but to locate shoals of fish as well. This has almost insured that a catch will be made and since 1945 has led to the development of the factory vessel, where the trawl is taken aboard over the stern and the catch is then immediately sorted and cleaned, ready for marketing or deep freezing.

Apart from ordinary fishing, man has also hunted the great mammals of the sea for about a thousand years.

There are old representations of dolphins which, however, do not prove that these mammals were caught. Our oldest information on whaling comes from Norway in about the year 900 A.D. A medal from the town of Biarritz describes whaling by the Basques in the year 1351. This, however, tells of small whales only, in addition to fishing for blackfish in the Faroe Islands. After William Poole, in 1583, and William Barents, in 1596, reported a great number of Greenland whales off Spitzbergen during their searches for the Northwest Passage, the British, in 1611, and the Dutch, in 1612, began an intensive hunt for whales. The Germans, in 1643, and the Americans, in 1650, also joined the hunt. Whale blubber was boiled to produce whale oil, at first on the Arctic islands, later in the homeland and also on shipboard. The actual pursuit of whales was carried out from small, strongly built rowing boats which carried crews of six to eight. The men used hand harpoons as weapons. Dead whales were stripped of their blubber and the remains were then allowed to drift away.

In about the year 1863 a Norwegian whaler mounted a newly invented harpoon gun on a steam vessel, and this made it possible to harpoon the faster-moving blue whales and rorquals. The harpoon was fitted with an explosive charge so that a quick killing of the whales was possible, and in 1935 the harpoon was further improved by fitting it with an electrocuting device. In today's whaling, steam or motor-driven vessels with powerful engines are used. After the whales are harpooned, they are towed to a large mother ship (factory ship) where they are winched up a slipway in the stern onto the whale deck. A large whale which, with its 100-foot length, is the biggest mammal ever to have been seen on earth, is cut up mechanically and completely disposed of in less than an hour. The largest of these factory ships, the *Unitas,* has a capacity of 30,000 tons. Whale oil is kept in large tanks aboard such vessels.

Besides whaling, seal hunting on the ice was conducted in Polar regions. The same sort of vessel was used for this as for whaling. As in the development of whaling boats, barks and steamers and, after 1914, motor-driven ships were built for seal hunting. Formerly killed by being clubbed, these fur-bearing animals are now shot.

Because of its importance to the food supply, fishing has become an international economic pursuit. Many nations draw in the harvest of the sea. Their shipping must be protected from piracy even in restricted areas, and the catches should be worth while as to size. So that this can be accomplished, fishermen must have knowledge of the sea and its creatures. The surveys carried out by the International Commission for Marine Research, based on systematic deep-sea expeditions since 1872, serve this end. The International Commission, organized in 1902 by the Northern European countries, co-ordinates research on the basis of the following program:

1. Hydrographic work
2. Testing of equipment to be used
3. Biological work
4. Fishery statistics

Since 1945 this task has been taken over by the FAO (Food and Agricultural Organization) inside OEEC (Organization for European Economic Co-operation) and OECD (Organization for Economic Co-operation and Development), respectively.

Furthermore, all countries with an interest in fishing carry out marine research in varying degrees with vessels of different sizes. These research ships make extensive observations and echo-sounding examinations of the fishing grounds. In addition to other forms of information gathering, research is carried out which should one day provide man with new kinds of food, such as the utilization of plankton.

OLD FISHING IMPLEMENTS

1, 2 Primitive bone gorges or bait holders (The slight curving of 1 may possibly be the first step toward the more rounded gorge and, eventually, the bent hook)

3, 4 Bone hooks from the Paleolithic Age in Sweden, *circa* 4000 B.C.

5, 6 Hooks from the Neolithic Age in Sweden, *circa* 2000 B.C.

7 The oldest Mycenaean hook in the British Museum in London

8 Hook ready-made from the spur of an insect, Eurycantha Latro, New Guinea

9 Harpoon from the Paleolithic Age in Sweden, *circa* 4000 B.C.

10 Paleolithic harpoon with ornament; the flukes are worn off

11 Man fishing, sitting astride a blown-up goatskin (From Assyrian sculptures in the British Museum)

12 Carved piece of bark that has been used as a float for a net with coarse meshes

13 Stone sinker belonging to the same net (12 and 13 are finds from the Ancylus period in Finland, *circa* 6000 B.C.)

14 Old grain for spearing eels

15 Hand line, one of the oldest and most practical implements for cod-fishing

16 Wickerwork creel for catching eels; herring or mackerel spawn were used for bait

TYPES OF FISHING BOATS

1 German heur boat
2 Greek fishing boat from Mykonos
3 Open Spanish fishing boat (Felucca)
4 Small Norwegian sailing fishing boat

5 French lugger (chasse marée)
6 Line fishing boat, Swedish west coast, 1880
7 German North Sea ketch

8 Portuguese barkentine for the Grand Banks
9 American Bank schooner, 1900
10 French Grand Bank schooner
11 British steam trawler
12 Large French motor trawler

TYPES OF FISHING BOATS

13 British sailing trawler, about 1900
14 British motor trawler
15 American dragger
16 Swedish west coast trawler
17 Portuguese sardine steam drifter
18 British steam drifter
19 Norwegian motor fishing boat
20 German motor trawler
21 American seiner
22 British seiner
23 Dutch motor fishing boat
24 Fishing boat from the Sound
25 Danish motor fishing boat
26 American troller
27 Japanese bonito boat
28 Norwegian motor fishing boat (Ottring)

TYPES OF FISHING BOATS

29 Spanish steam tunny boat
30 French tunny yawl
31 American tuna clipper
32 Sailing whaler, a three-masted bark, 1850
33 Modern whaler
34 Whaling factory ship
35 Norwegian sealer

OLD FISHING METHODS AND IMPLEMENTS

A *Mark buoy*
  1 Flag
  2 Pole
  3 Cork float
  4 Shackle for buoy line
B *Torch lamp*

C *Trawling for mackerel,*
   about 1880
  1 Fishing smack
  2 Quarter pole
  3 Main pole
  4 Bow pole
  5 Trawling lines
  6 Lead sinkers
  7 Snells

D *Shark hook*
E *Whaling harpoon with*
   hinged barb
F *Whaling harpoon*

G *Cod bow net*
  1 Cod end
  2 Rattan rings
  3 Headline
  4 Leading net
  5 Footrope

FISHING METHODS

A *Fishing with seine net of Scandinavian type*
a Setting the seine
b Hauling the warps
c Before hoisting the seine on board

1 Anchor buoy
2 Warps
3 Net tails
4 Seine purse
5 Seine netter

B *Fishing with purse seine*
1 Carrier
2 Purse seine netter
3 Floats
4 Cork line (headline)
5 Skiff
6 Leadline (footrope)
7 Purse line

FISHING METHODS

A *Fishing for mackerel with drift nets*
1 Mark buoy with flag
2 Buoy line
3 Floats
4 Net ends ("heads")
5 Nets
6 Headline ("back")
7 Footrope ("foot")
8 Drifter shooting nets

B *Long line fishing from dories*
1 Attending vessel
2 Dory with fishermen
3 Ground line
4 Snells

C *Long line fishing for halibut*
1 Buoy
2 Mark buoy
3 Motor fishing boat
4 Buoy rope
5 Anchor
6 Ground line
7 Snells

A

B

7

8

6

C

5

D

2

1

4

5

3

4

5

FISHING METHODS

A *Beam trawl, about 1800*
1 Stone weight
2 Belly
3 Beam
4 Wooden hoops

B *Modern floating trawl*
1 Cod end
2 Belly
3 Headline
4 Wings
5 Footrope
6 Weights
7 Towing warps
8 Motor trawlers,
  trawling in pairs

C *Otter trawl*
1 Cod end
2 Belly
3 Headline
4 Otter boards
5 Trawl warps
6 Steam trawler, about
  1900

D *Beam trawl, from the
  19th century*
1 Cod end
2 Belly
3 Beam
4 Trawl heads
5 Towing warps

FISH AND OTHER MARINE CREATURES

1 Seal	8 Bergylt	14 Red snapper
2 Bluefish	9 Ray	15 Conger eel
3 Tunny	10 Greenland whale	16 Great barracuda
4 Albacore	11 Polyprion	17 Dogfish
5 Angler	Americanum	18 Sole
6 Ray's bream	12 Salmon	19 Shark
7 Wrasse	13 Octopus	

FISH AND OTHER MARINE CREATURES

20 Mackerel	27 Sea cat	33 Oyster
21 Turbot	28 Prawn	34 Haddock
22 Cod	29 Halibut	35 Burbot
23 Herring	30 Plaice	36 Ling
24 Whiting	31 Crab	37 Coalfish
25 Brill	32 Hake	38 Sprat
26 Lobster		39 Sardine

The picture of Star
boats in a race, taken
by KEY L. NILSSON,
introduces the chapter
on yachting.

YACHTING

BY GEORGE P. B. NAISH

The word yacht nowadays usually refers to privately owned pleasure craft, used either for racing or cruising. There are still royal or state owned yachts, but before the 19th century the word usually referred to vessels publicly owned and used for the conveyance of princes, ambassadors, or other great personages from one kingdom to another. The word yacht came into the English language from the Netherlands at the time of the restoration of King Charles II to the throne in 1660. But, of course, ships and boats had been used for purposes of state and for pleasure from earliest times.

Thus, the model of a yacht used on the river Nile by an Egyptian nobleman of the 18th Dynasty, some 1500 years B.C. has been found in a tomb. It is represented as a vessel of a hundred feet in length over all, elaborately decorated and painted, with a deckhouse for a cabin. This yacht was probably used by the nobleman while traveling up and down the Nile valley on business. Egyptian tombs also depict small pleasure craft, which could be towed either from the bank or astern of other vessels. Perhaps Cleopatra's barge, which she used when she first met Antony, should be classed as a yacht. Plutarch tells us that the poop was of gold, the sails of purple, and the oars of silver. In English history we read of King Edgar, who reigned from 959 to 975 A.D., being rowed on the river Dee by a crew of eight lesser kings. But on the whole, in early times people seldom went to sea for pleasure, for there were too many dangers either from storms or from pirates.

The modern pleasure yacht was first developed as a type in Holland, with its maze of rivers and meres, on which, according to the many pictures painted in the seventeenth century, scores of shallow draft sailing boats, gaily carved and decorated, were raced and shown. There were also large state-owned yachts, and in 1660 one of these, originally built for the East India Company, was bought by the City of Amsterdam for presentation to the restored King of England. Both James I and Charles I had taken a great interest in shipbuilding and naval affairs generally and Charles II first learned to sail as a boy in a pinnace off the island of Jersey. He had continued to distract himself with sailing during his exile in Holland. The gift yacht from Amsterdam was named the *Mary,* and was a typical Dutch state yacht of a hundred tons, broad in the beam and of shallow draft with lee boards. The stern cabin had a high coach roof and windows. The stern was decorated with the royal arms, surmounted by three poop lanterns, and the figurehead was a unicorn. Eight little guns could be fired from circular gunports, each decorated with carved and gilded port wreaths. The *Mary* was cutter, or yacht rigged, and carried a boomless mainsail with a long standing gaff, called a half-spreet. The next year the Dutch gave Charles

a smaller yacht, the *Bezan,* with the bezaan rig, well known in Holland, with a boomed mainsail and a short gaff. Charles soon set English shipwrights to building yachts which for English waters were an improvement in that they had deeper draft instead of leeboards. The new English royal yachts were much like small warships, but retained the fore-and-aft rig

When Charles tired of a yacht it was received into the fleet as a dispatch vessel or survey ship. Charles took much pleasure in his yachts, either for racing or making trips, and his brother James, Duke of York, as well as certain private gentlemen, followed his example and became owners of yachts. Several private individuals explored the English coast or visited the Continent in the second half of the 17th century.

When Peter the Great, Tzar of Russia, studied shipbuilding in Holland and England he learned his seamanship in yachts, and the French king, Louis XIV, had yachts built for him in England.

Although yachting for pleasure showed no signs of becoming a popular sport in the 18th century, it managed to hold its own in English waters despite the many long wars. There were river pageants, and in 1775 the Cumberland Fleet or sailing society was founded by the royal Duke of that name, who offered a cup for a regatta between some twenty small yachts of from two to five tons which was held on the river Thames above London Bridge. The Royal Thames Yacht Club claims descent from this Cumberland Fleet. The Fleet's yachts were distinguished by special pennants and the owners wore smart nautical uniforms.

We find William Hickey sailing in a cutter yacht of fifty tons in 1768: "a heavy dull sailer, but with capital accommodation, having a spacious cabin aft her whole width with sash windows astern."

Greenwich was considered the harbor for royal yachts during the century, and from Greenwich the royal family sailed for Hanover. George III reviewed his fleet at the Nore in 1781, sailing down the Thames with a flotilla of three or four royal yachts. In the National Maritime Museum at Stockholm the stern and king's cabin of Gustav III's schooner, the *Amphion,* built in 1778, is preserved, along with its furniture. The King held many councils of war in this cabin, when fighting the Russians in 1790.

The 19th century marked the beginning of yacht racing as a great international sport. In 1815 the peace with France no doubt encouraged the formation in England of the Royal Yacht Squadron, under royal patronage, with

its headquarters at Cowes, Isle of Wight, which faced the sheltered waters of the Solent. The members were rich men owning large yachts, which were designed to resemble the brigs and schooners and cutters of the royal navy. The members considered, in fact, that one of their duties was to improve the design of sailing ships for the benefit of the royal navy. Mr. Dixon Kemp, a famous writer on yachting subjects, who died in 1899, estimated there were some 50 British yachts afloat in 1800 and as many as 503 in 1850. These yachts averaged some fifty tons apiece; they were mostly cutters with bluff bows and lines which fined off aft, the well-known "cod's head and mackerel's tail" fashion.

In 1851, the American schooner *America* was sailed to Cowes and raced around the Isle of Wight for a cup presented by the Royal Yacht Squadron. The *America* had her dazzling white cotton sails cut to stand flat as boards, in opposition to the very full cut English flax sails. And she had a light displacement and fine lines fore and aft. She won the cup and her example helped to revolutionize yacht design in European waters. In particular, her long hollow bow was copied.

Racing yachts were now built with deeper and narrower midship sections. The iron ballast was replaced by lead, and this lead began to be put on the keel instead of being interior ballast. A famous and successful yacht was the *Jullanar,* built in 1875, the design concentrating on a short keel, a long water line, and the smallest frictional surface. By the end of the century the old, narrow vessels, with their heavy weight and deep forward section and lean bow water lines, were useless when racing against the new lighter, broader boats. These new racing boats were becoming veritable skimming dishes, until a sensible compromise was effected; then the profile was rounded up forward and a raking sternpost was built aft so as to cut down the wetted surface.

It was calculated there were some 2,000 yachts in the British Isles by 1881 amounting to 100,000 tons, that is, an average of 50 tons a yacht. These were built at a cost of some £50 a ton, and were only half the tonnage of sailing yachts. By now, the steam yacht had become popular, and Lord Brassey's auxiliary three-masted schooner, the *Sunbeam* made a number of world cruises, the first in 1878, which were popularized by the narratives published by Lady Brassey.

By the beginning of the 20th century yachting had become an international sport, as popular in the United States as in the British Isles, and was spreading to the Mediterranean and Baltic and the great sheltered harbors of Australia and New Zealand. Anglo-American yachting rivalry is most well known in the America's Cup races.

The first of these was held under the auspices of the New York Yacht Club in 1870.

Yachting in America had begun a rapid expansion once the Civil War was over, and in 1866 three rival schooners, the *Vesta, Henrietta,* and the *Fleetwing,* raced from Sandy Hook to Cowes Roads, arriving within nine hours of each other, although the *Fleetwing* had had six men swept out of her cockpit by a heavy sea. Naturally the great schooners caught the public eye and their doings were recorded in the press.

To many people the word yachting summoned up a picture of a fashionable gathering, for example, Cowes Week, with the roads full of large steam yachts, house parties on board, and fleets of sailing craft racing by day and returning to their moorings each night, so that the owners could attend social gatherings at the various yacht clubs. Serious yacht racing in the big classes had no more keen supporters than King Edward VII and King George V, who owned the famous racing cutter *Britannia,* designed by George Watson, between 1893 and 1935.

The German Kaiser came over to England to race, manning his yachts with English crews. Principally owing to the enthusiasm of King George V, the splendid great "J" Class cutters were raced again after the 1914-1918 war. These large yachts were generally manned by professional crews and became increasingly expensive to run. Therefore, it was not surprising that the trend turned toward building smaller, cheaper yachts, which could be manned and often partially maintained by amateur crews. And at the same time, racing in really small boats became increasingly popular; this popularity has become very obvious since World War II, because it is possible to race the modern dinghy on such small stretches of water as are formed by reservoirs and old gravel pits. It is now quite usual to sight a mass of small white sails earnestly engaged in yacht racing although they are far from the open sea.

In 1963 the International Yacht Racing Union consists of more than fifty different countries, including the Union of Soviet Socialist Republics and the United Arab Republic. There are eight international classes, including the 12-meters, the famous Dragons of Norwegian design, and the 14-foot international racing dinghy. Popular classes of small yachts, which can be used for racing or cruising, include the Folkbåts, a very popular and successful Swedish design, and the Vertue, product of a Solent yard.

While yacht racing is more likely to figure in the newspapers, cruising yachts have existed certainly from the 17th century, when we find an English naval officer fit-

ting out his ship's boat and proceeding up the Channel with his dog for crew and company. He armed his boat with a swivel gun against pirates, and fired this off as a salute when entering Rye harbor in the early morning, so that the townsfolk manned their defences under the impression that the man and dog were themselves marauders. Since then, cruising yachtsmen have included many odd characters, including men who chose to sail single-handed, sometimes crossing oceans, sometimes exploring difficult coastlines. The more famous of them include Captain Joshua Slocum, who sailed alone around the world in the *Spray,* 1896 to 1898. He was a citizen of the United States who built his own ship in Fairhaven, Massachusetts, by carefully copying an old hull pulled up into a field. Captain Voss made his venturesome voyages in a converted Indian dugout canoe, looking for heavy weather so that he could try out a sea anchor and the effects of pouring oil on troubled waters. Frank Cowper wrote of enchanting sailing tours, combining near-fiction and detailed sailing directions for the coasts of the United Kingdom and Brittany. McMullen sailed heavy luggers up and down the English Channel, "single-handed," for when his wife sailed with him he did not care to count her as his crew. Rob Roy MacGregor not only popularized a type of canoe but built himself a small yawl and wrote a narrative which inspired others to follow his example. These men were on the scene in the closing years of the 19th century, and their example has proved infectious.

Dr. Claud Worth was one of the first of the amateur yachtsmen who turned his scientific training—for he was an eye specialist—toward inquiry into the proper design for yachts and the best materials from which to build them, the proper fastenings and all the details of the fittings connected with the rigging, the ground tackle—everything, in fact, upon which the safety of the yacht at sea depended. Dr. Worth wanted an ocean-going cruising yacht.

The rapid increase of interest in ocean racing and the problems this has posed has also had an important and beneficial effect on the sport as a whole. The object has been to produce small yachts intended to race on the open sea in all weathers. Early successes—the first Fastnet Race was held in 1925—went to converted pilot cutters.

The typical Bristol Channel pilot cutter had a large beam and draft, interior ballast only, and had been developed to establish sea-kindliness and the ability to keep the sea in all weathers. As these cutters had to be worked with a small crew, the mast was stepped well aft, which required a large fore staysail, perhaps the easiest sail in the ship to handle. In a breeze, these cutters were fast and weatherly, but often wet because of over ballasting. But they

were very slow in light weather, so that when the specially designed light displacement ocean racers were built, the heavy old pilot cutters soon went out of business as ocean racers. The new ocean racers had all their ballast in the keel, many suits of headsails, such as genoas and spinnakers, and beautifully cut Bermudan mainsails, which did away with the weight of the gaff aloft. However, the influence of the older pilot cutters is still great on cruising yachts, a famous example being the *Dyarchy,* built in Sweden in 1939 to the design of Laurent Giles and partners. Nowadays, some small yachts with amateur crews will be racing across oceans, while others, perhaps crewed by a man and his wife, will be circumnavigating the world. The sport is on the increase and the meres and rivers of Holland are as busy with small craft as they were in the 17th century.

The sheltered waters of the Baltic are ideal for yachting, while in the Mediterranean the age-old harbors of Venice or Alexandria have their yacht berths in the same way as do the more modern harbors of New York or Sydney. Motor yachting, which can be quickly learned, attracts as many persons as does the sailing yacht. There are a great many standard craft on the market, and the outboard motor enables many hulls to be quickly converted into power boats. Materials, such as fiber glass, make it possible for hulls to be mass-produced. Fabrics, such as Dacron, prolong the life of sails. And the twin hulls of the catamaran have provided new thrills by letting small yachts sail very fast indeed with just a beam wind. There may be something new coming out every month, but the conditions of wind and weather remain the same, and it is important that the many yacht clubs exercise some sort of control to insure that yachtsmen sail the seas in seaworthy craft. Seamanlike precautions are to be preferred to foolhardy risks.

No doubt the general introduction of the auxiliary motor into most large sailing yachts has diminished the risk of shipwreck or collision, but it has also made it possible for yachts to cruise very much further in a given period.

HEADBOARD MUST NOT COME ABOVE BLACK BAND

BODY PLAN (OR FRAME SECTIONS)
TO OUTSIDE OF PLANK.

MAXIMUM ANGLE PERMITTED 130°

PLAN VIEW OF TUMPER STRUTS.

The form of Sections 4, 8, 10½ & 12 must be according to Plan, and will be checked by Moulds
Width over deck must be ÷
At Section 4 – 4'-9¾" (1.468 M)
   "   "   8' – 6'-5" (1.958 M)
   "   "   10½ – 5'-10½" (1.792 M)
   "   "   12 – 5'-1" (1.550 M)
Length overall – 29'-2½" (+5% = 29'-4¼") (8.948 M)
(8.900 M)

INTERNATIONAL "DRAGON" CLASS

SAIL AND RIGGING PLAN

SCALE :– 1:24.

SAIL AREAS

MAINSAIL	171·1 SQ FEET	(15·9 m²)
FORESAIL Nº 1	64·6 "	(8·0 ")
FORESAIL Nº 2	45·2 "	(4·2 ")
GENOA	115·1 "	(10·7 ")
SPINAKER	253·9 "	(23·6 ")

THE INTERNATIONAL DRAGON CLASS

The Dragon is a very popular class of one-design, fixed-keel boat, and in Europe today the International Dragon class is probably the largest group of such boats. It was designed as early as 1929 by the Norwegian designer, Johan Anker, at the request of the Royal Yacht Club of Gothenburg. The class soon spread to all Scandinavia and Germany, and in 1935 it was introduced into Great Britain. The control of the class is administered by the International Yacht Racing Union.

The aim of the Dragon was to get a racing cruiser with a high speed and a cabin for two. At the same time, the boat is very seaworthy and able to carry her large sail, even in strong winds. The hull of the Dragon has not been altered, but the rigging was changed in 1946.

MATERIALS AND SCANTLINGS

KEEL: STEM & STERN COUNTER TIMBER OAK, MOULDED 50% (2") SIDED AS TO FORM

PLANKING. 17% (%")

BENT FRAMES. 25% × 30% (1" × 1%") FOR HALF LENGTH AMIDSHIPS, AT ENDS 22% × 25% (%" × 1")

TWO GROWN OR BENT FRAMES ABREAST THE MAST MOULDED 30% × 34% (1%" × 1%")

FLOORS. OAK SIDED 70% (2%") FOR THE LENGTH OF THE BALLAST KEEL & 50% (2") BEYOND THE KEEL.

DECK. AS RULES.

COVERING BOARD MAHOGANY 95% × 14% (3½" × %")

COAMING MAHOGANY 16% (%")

DECK BEAMS SPACING 250% (10") CENTRE TO CENTRE. SEE PLAN

CARLING 50% × 40% (2" × 1%")

SHELF 27% × 100% (1%" × 3%") OR 24% × 115% (%" × 4½")

PLANKING TO BE FASTENED TO FRAMES WITH COPPER NAILS 1½ LONG CLENCHED ON ROOVES OR
WITH Nº 11 BRASS SCREWS 1" LONG. KEEL, FLOORS, STEM ETC FASTENING BRASS SCREWS Nº 11 - 1½

KEEL BOLTS GALVANISED ROUND IRON

FRAME SPACING 200% (7%") CENTRE TO CENTRE

AS FOR MATERIALS SEE SPECIFICATION

FRAMES AT THE SECTIONS 4, 8 & 12 ARE TO BE OF ASH, OAK OR ELM MOULDED
TO 30 M/M × 34 M/M (1³/₁₆" × 1³/₈"). IF OF OAK THEY SHALL BE LAMINATED OR GROWN.
IF OF ASH OR ELM THEY SHALL BE LAMINATED.

INTERNATIONAL "DRAGON" CLASS
CONSTRUCTION PLAN

OFFICIAL SET OF 7 BUILDING PLANS (PRICE 39/-
SURFACE POST FREE) ARE OBTAINABLE FROM THE
INTERNATIONAL YACHT RACING UNION OR THE ROYAL
YACHTING ASSOCIATION BOTH AT 171 VICTORIA
STREET, LONDON, S.W.1.

DRAGON RACES

The International Dragon Gold Cup was initiated in 1936, and is competed for annually in Britain, Norway, Sweden, or Denmark. Since 1948, the Dragon has been used at the Olympic Games, where the class now is the most popular.

The Edinburgh Cup was presented by the Duke of Edinburgh in 1949 for competition in Britain. The Herriot Cup was offered by the Yacht Club of France in 1948.

OLD YACHTS

A *Dutch yacht, 1678*

B *The Swedish state barge, Vasaorden, constructed in 1774 by af Chapman for King Gustavus III*

C *The famous schooner yacht, America, which in 1851 won the Queen's Cup, later known as the America's Cup. The America was a development from the American East Coast pilot schooner.*

D *The American schooner, Sappho, defender of the America's Cup in 1871*

E *Shamrock IV, owned by Sir Thomas Lipton, the British challenger in the Cup race of 1920*

F *H.M. Yacht, Britannia, in her first rig; she was built in 1893 for the Prince of Wales, later Edward VII*

G *Jolie Brise, winner of the first Fastnet Race and founder of the R.O.R.C. Rule*

H *The development of hull profiles*

1 *Shortfoot, a British yacht from the beginning of the 19th century*

2 *America, 1851*

3 *Jullanar, English yawl, 126 tons TM, built in 1875*

4 *Gloriana, 133 tons, constructed by Nathaniel Herreshoff, Rhode Island, 1891*

OLD AND NEW LARGE YACHTS

1 The *Drott*, built in 1877 and rebuilt in 1883 for the Swedish king, Oscar II

2 The British Royal yacht, *Victoria and Albert*, built in 1899

3 The Royal Danish yacht, *Dannebrog*, built in 1931

4 The motor yacht, *Vedette*, built at Copenhagen in 1924 for Fred W. Vanderbilt, New York

5 The *Stella Polaris*, for tourist cruises

6 The British Royal yacht, *Britannia*, built in 1954

7 The three-masted fore-and-aft schooner, *Sunbeam II*, built in 1929 for Lord Runciman; now a Swedish training ship under the name *Flying Clipper*, rigged as a topsail schooner

YACHT FITTINGS

A *A new type of spin- B* *Combination bow light   D* *Log register   F* *Rubber fender*
   naker, with downward C *Hand-held anemometer   E* *Inglefield clips   G* *Windlass*
   jet thrust for greater
   lift and driving power

YACHT FITTINGS

A Elastic gasket with
   wood toggle

B Light metal fitting on
   masthead for shrouds
   and spreader

C Roller-reefing gear of
   stainless steel
   1 Mast
   2 Boom
   3 Roller-reefing gear
   4 Mast track
   5 Eye bolt for tack
   6 Bolt for tack cringle of
      sail
   7 Detachable handle

D Sheet and parrel on
   boom with roller-
   reefing
   1 Boom
   2 Parrel
   3 Trundles
   4 Foot of sail
   5 Sheet
   6 Sail rolled on boom

MODERN SAILING YACHTS

1 Star	5 Moth (British)	10 14 ft. dinghy	14 Firefly	17 International 6-meter yacht	21 J.O.G.
2 Snipe	6 Moth (American)	11 Flying Fifteen	15 Swallow	18 International OD-class	22 Cruising yacht
3 Swordfish	7 International canoe	12 12 ft. class	16 International 12-meter yacht (Weatherly)	19 Y W Cadet	23 International 5.5-meter yacht
4 Tumlaren	8 8 ft. register class	13 Merlin/Rocket class		20 Ketch	24 Yawl
	9 12 sq. m. class				

A SELECTION OF ONE-DESIGN YACHTS

1 Blue Jay	6 Rhodes Bantam	11 Thistle	16 OK-dinghy	20 Korsar	24 Killingen
2 Comet	7 Sailfish	12 Folkboat	17 Pirate dinghy	21 Oslo-dinghy	25 7 m Sperrholzjollen-
3 Dyer Dhow	8 Flying Junior	13 Finn	18 30 sq. m. Danish	22 30 sq. m. skärgårds-	kreuzer (plywood
4 5 O 5	9 Flying Dutchman	14 Wood Pussy	double-ender	kryssare	cruiser)
5 Lightning	10 Triton	15 Knarr	19 Swedish double-ender	23 Einheitselbjolle	26 6.5 KR-Seekreuzer
			(not one-design)		(not one-design)

YACHT RACING

A The course of the America's Cup
1 First, this course is sailed windward and leeward twice
2 Then, the triangular course is sailed once
3 Start and finish. The direction of the wind is supposed to be southwest.
4 6-mile circle
5 8-mile circle

B A common type of racing course
A, B, or C is start- and finishing-line. 1—9 and U, Y, and Z are rounding buoys. The red lines give the boundary of the courses. The inset signboard with letters and figures is the course-board, which is placed at the starting center.

The signboard shows the following course: After the start over the B line the following buoys are to be rounded: 1, the buoy B of the starting line, 1 and 3, after which C is used for a finishing line. A red or blue field to the right indicates whether the buoys are to be

taken on the port or on the starboard side of the boat. (This example shows the racing courses at Marstrand, Sweden.)

C The courses of the Olympic Games
At the Olympic Races 8 buoys are laid out in a circle with a radius of 1 nautical mile. In this arrangement the starting place and the rounding buoys may be varied, depending upon the direction of the wind. In the diagrams

the wind blows from the west, so the boats start at buoy No. 3. At first, a triangular course is sailed, 3—7—5—3 (CI), and then a windward and leeward course, 3—7—3 (CII), and finally a windward course from 3 to the finish at 7 (CIII).

RULES OF YACHT RACING

A Starting boat should lie on the wind or, when starting, in fair wind steering for the first buoy

1, 2, and 3 are starting correctly

At the start 3 is allowed to force 4 outside the buoy (See C)

5 is sailing on the port tack and has to give way to 1, 2, 3, and 4

6 has to give way to the others

7. Not a permitted course at the start

B If two boats are sailing on different tacks the one which has the wind on the port side has to give way to the other

1, 2, and 3 should give way to 4

C Exception from B
When rounding a buoy 1 has to give way to 2, if the stem of the overtaking boat has passed athwart of the stern of the leading boat

Exception: at start (See A)

D Some definitions
1 is astern of 2
The stem of 3 has passed the athwartship line of the stern of 4 and 3 should give way to 4 except when they are rounding a buoy (See C) By hauling her wind, 4 is allowed to

block 3's hawse. When the mast of 5 is abeam the helmsman of 6, 5 must not luff any more but should bear up (toward the buoy)

E If the distance between the boats is less than 3 boat lengths 1 must not restrain 2 from trying to pass to leeward

CATAMARAN AND SOME YACHT DETAILS

A *Catamarans*
1 Catamaran of Cougar Class
2 Asymmetrical catamaran; the flat outside acts as a centerboard
3 Symmetrical catamaran with centerboard

B *Steering gear of a big racing yacht*
C *Flattop deck winch*

D *Forged turnbuckle*
E *Yacht block of plastic laminate and stainless steel*

F *Halliard winch, as fitted on mast*
G *Danforth anchor*

H *Transistorized radio direction finder*

A

D

E

B

C

SOME YACHT CLUB FLAGS AND YACHT FITTINGS

A *Flags*
1 Royal Yacht Squadron
2 Cruising Yacht Club of Australia
3 New York Yacht Club
4 Yacht Club of France
5 United States Yacht Ensign

B *Yachting blocks of stainless steel*

C *Vertical card compass for small boats*
D *Ice yacht*

E *Yacht of the Ljung-ström type*
This type of boat often had a streamlined hull and a rotating mast without stays, around which the sails were rolled when they were taken in. The sail was *double and had no boom. When the wind was right aft it was carried wing and wing, as shown in the diagram.*

CRUISING YACHT

Cruising yacht designed by Sparkman & Stephens and built for a French owner, total length 40 ft., length on water line 29 ft., breadth 10 ft., draft 6½ ft., displacement 7.69 tons, lead keel 3.37 tons

A Perspective drawing of of hull as seen from below from the starboard bow and from the port quarter

B Sail plan, area of sails 533 square feet (according to international rules)

1 Main sail, 258 square feet
2 Jib No. 1, 237 square feet
3 Jib No. 2, 135 square feet
4 Genoa No. 1, 327 square feet

5 Genoa No. 2, 381 square feet
6 Storm staysail
7 Storm trysail

Engine, 25 hp at 4,800 r.p.m., 1.71:1 reduction gear

CRUISING YACHT

1	Lead keel	7	Tiller	14	Fo'c'sle
2	Rudder	8	Galley	15	Wardrobe
3	Propeller	9	Berth	16	Lockers
4	Engine	10	Table	17	Fresh water
5	Frames	11	Mast	18	Fuel
6	Cockpit with binnacle	12	Lavatory	19	Hatch to sail locker
		13	Saloon		

MOTORBOAT TYPES

1 Small wooden boat with inboard motor	4 Outboard fiberglass racing boat	8 66 ft. motor cruiser	12 30 ft. cruiser with two inboard motors
2 Undecked laminated fiberglass plastic boat	5 Wooden cabin boat with outboard motor	9 25 ft. inboard cabin boat	13 Outboard racer
3 Small outboard fiber-glass boat	6 36 ft. motor cruiser	10 120 ft. motor cruiser	14 20 ft. plywood boat
	7 Fifty-fifty cruiser	11 Sport fisherman	15 Inboard racer
			16 Houseboat

MOTORBOAT DETAILS

A *Outside view of modern outboard motor*

B *Inside view of outboard motor*
 1 Starting wire
 2 Flywheel
 3 Crankcase
 4 Cylinders
 5 Spark plugs
 6 Strut
 7 Cooling pipe
 8 Exhaust
 9 Propeller shaft
10 Fin
11 Ahead pinion
12 Reverse pinion
13 Gear housing
14 Shaft
15 Reverse pawl
16 Angular setting
17 Securing clamps
18 Tiller

C *Safety ski flag*
   Approved by American Water Ski Association; signifies that the boat is pulling water skier

D *Inboard-outboard engine*

E *Depth-distance indicator*
   This indicator shows both soundings and horizontal distances

F *Radar for small craft*

G *Variable-pitch propeller*

H *Aerosol-powered foghorn*

A detail from an etching illustrating the battle on the Sound on October 29, 1658, appropriately introduces the chapter on gunnery. The etching was obtained from Histoire de Charles X by Pufendorf.

GUNNERY

BY ALAN W H. PEARSALL

Sea warfare was at first carried on with the same weapons used on land: arrows, darts, javelins, swords, and lances; and the combatants wore the customary armor to protect themselves against their opponents' attacks. Sea warfare was largely fought by soldiers, who employed military methods and tactics.

From the 14th century onward the gun became the weapon most in use. Early guns were made of iron bars forged together and lashed by metal strapping. They were usually breech loaders, and were mounted on wooden fulcrums. They fired round stone shot. Such guns were used on the bows of galleys, and to some extent along the broadside of the newly developed North European fighting ship.

By the 16th century methods of manufacture had improved so that gun barrels could be cast in one piece; and from the 17th century the bore was hollowed out after casting. These guns were muzzle-loading, to give added strength; and, with more effective gunpowder, had a much greater range. In experienced hands, these guns could be fired almost once every minute. They

fired solid round shot, usually made of iron, but other destructive types of ammunition were used as well. Still, the manufacture of such guns was not sufficiently precise for great accuracy of aim. These guns were the chief armament of ships for nearly three hundred years. They used a carriage of two vertical brackets connected by suitable crosspieces, the whole mounted on four wheels. Many such guns, like the classic cannon, survived into the next era. They were then primarily used as broadside guns.

Special types of ordnance were used for particular purposes. Short guns, called mortars, fired at an elevation of about forty-five degrees. They threw shells into towns or ports and were fitted on especially protected ships. These shells were hollow round shot, filled with powder and fired by a time fuse. Howitzers fired shells, too, but from ordinary carriages at a lower elevation. About 1779 carronades were introduced. These were cannon which had a short barrel, thus lightening the weight of the artillery while allowing heavy shot to be fired. However, this was accomplished at the expense of length of range. Small swivel guns were also used to fire at an enemy's decks;

these guns had a stock and butt like a musket, and pivoted on a swivel fitted into sockets in the bulwarks.

The 19th century brought revolutionary developments in arms at sea. Smooth-bore guns were increasingly used for firing shells and, with an increase in the size of guns, came the introduction of armored ships. Thus began a long race between gun and armor. Rifling was the first of these important changes. With its aid, accuracy increased and a more thorough use of the propulsive power of powder was made. To get the most out of both accuracy and power breech-loading was adopted, so that longer barrels, which were built up of coils, and a very tight fit of the projectile in the barrel were possible. Various types of breech were tried, and despite some difficulties, breech-loading guns were in use by all navies by 1880.

Gun carriages showed parallel developments. The old wooden type gave way to a pivot-slide carriage, and this was now made of iron to take the weight of increasingly larger guns. But the carriages were cumbersome, and a suitable substitute had to be found. This was the turret and its variants, by which guns were mounted inside an armored structure which turned on ball bearings. Such mountings revolutionized the design of ships, which had already begun a period of transformation with the introduction of armor and the increasing size of guns. The larger guns led naturally to a reduction in the number of guns needed. These same factors made it necessary for designers to use machinery for elevating, training, and loading the guns.

At the end of the 19th century, there was a trend toward the use of small rapid-firing guns. This kind of gun used a cartridge which contained an explosive charge and the projectile to be fired, both in a brass case. Previously, the charge of powder in a silk bag had been loaded separately from the shot. Also in this period many types of machine gun appeared, such as the Nordenfeldt, Gardner, Gatling, and Maxim. Many of these pieces had several barrels.

Projectiles changed enormously. Round shot was replaced by long cylindrical shells with pointed noses. The explosive power of these shells was vastly greater in destructive force; some were made with re-inforced noses so as to pierce armor, others contained bullets for use against personnel, and the fuses by which they were exploded became more complicated.

The introduction of improvements in powder brought important changes, one being a smokeless powder which kept the battle area fairly clear.

The war of 1914—1918 represented the culmination of this era. From this time on, the gun was the center of a system, as all its artillery functions were worked by mechanical means; the individual gun was now directed by increasingly complex fire-control systems. Further improvements were made in the construction and mechanism of the modern gun so that it had a vastly greater accuracy.

Other important branches of armament were carried in ships. In the 18th century carcasses, or floating explosive charges, were sometimes used, as were also fire and explosion ships. In the early 19th century rockets were first employed in this more brutal kind of warfare.

Mines, then called torpedoes, were used in the American Civil War and subsequently refined in various ways, some being controlled from shore, others depending on contact with or later still a mere proximity to a ship. The actuating machinery of these mines varied. A crude form of the torpedo proper was also used in the American Civil War. Various other types were subsequently tried, such as towing and spar torpedoes. However, the invention of the locomotive torpedo, which gave greater range and caused less danger to the attacker, rapidly gained predominance. It was also developed so as to increase its speed, range, and accuracy, and with a variety of firing mechanisms so that modern torpedoes are able to "home" on their target.

DIRIGE MEVM

16·31

GUN WITH ACCESSORIES, 1691 (FROM Å.C. RÅLAMB)

1 Cartridge	5 Bar-shot	11 Tompion	18 Quoin	24 Powder horn	30 Musket ball bag
2 Case-shot	6 Peak shot	12 Cascabel	19 Funnel	25 Lint stock	31 Shot grommet
3 Bar-shot	7 Hand grenade	13 Trunnions	20 Powder measure	26 Lint stock of iron	32 Powder keg
4 Chain-shot	8 Section of ship's side	14 Gun carriage	21 Vent bit	27 Shot gauge	33 Hand spike
	9 Gun	15 Train tackles	22 Vent auger	28 Rammer and sponge	34 Gun ladle
	10 Muzzle	16 Breeching	23 Priming wire, reamer	29 Fire grommet	35 Rammer and sponge
		17 Bed			

GUNS, 1870-1915

A *Smooth bore gun (about 1870)*
1 Gun, cannon
2 Mounting
3 Elevating hand wheel
4 Loading crane
5 Loading tray
6 Shot

B *7.5 cm (3″) Bofors gun (1915)*
1 Barrel
2 Jacket
3 Cradle
4 Range wheel
5 Gunsight telescope
6 Deflection wheel
7 Breech

8 Control mechanism
9 Elevation gear
10 Training gear
11 Recoil brake
12 Mounting
13 Elevating gear
14 Firing device
15 Breech block

C *7.5 cm high-explosive charge (H.E. charge)*
1 Cartridge
2 Fuse
3 Detonator
4 Charge
5 Shell
6 Rotating band (driving band)

MODERN GUN

A *Automatic gun in twin
  mounting* (12 cm)
1 Axis of bore
2 Muzzle
3 Barrel
4 Twin guns

5 Cradle
6 Turret
7 Breech
8 Recoil brake
9 Ammunition hoist
  motor

10 Ammunition hoist
11 Training motor
12 Magazine
13 Pivot

B *Ammunition*
1 Nose fuse
2 Detonator
3 Shell
4 Charge
5 Rotating band
  (driving band)

6 Propellant charge
7 Primer
8 Ballistic cap

COAST DEFENCE SHIP, 1922

Swedish coast defense battleship Gustaf V, displacement, 7275 tons, from a drawing by Gösta Kaudern in Svenska Flottans Historia

1 Forecastle deck
2 Windlass
3 Twin gun turret (11 inches)
4 Rangefinder
5 Anti-aircraft gun
6 Pilot bridge
7 Rangefinder
8 Conning tower (pilot turret)
9 Rangefinder
10 Signal bridge
11 Director control tower with rangefinder
12 Radio antenna
13 Stack
14 Motorboat
15 Boat davits
16 Searchlight
17 Radio direction finder
18 75 mm anti-aircraft gun
19 20 mm anti-aircraft gun
20 Director control tower for anti-aircraft gun
21 75 mm anti-aircraft gun
22 Twin gun turret (11 inches)
23 40 mm anti-aircraft gun
24 Smoke screen maker
25 Rudder
26 Propeller
27 Bilge keel
28 Paravane holder
29 Icebreaking stem
30 6 inch guns
31 Ammunition hoist
32 Barbette
33 Shell magazine
34 Powder magazine
35 Combat information center
36 Crew's quarters
37 Warrant officers' accommodation
38 Protective deck
39 Chain locker
40 Washroom
41 Pilot room
42 Boiler
43 Galley
44 Sick bay
45 Magazine
46 Generator
47 Coal bunker
48 Turbine
49 Reduction gearing
50 Radio office
51 Workroom
52 Operating rooms
53 Engineer's office
54 Officers' quarters
55 Wardroom
56 Cabin for the Admiral of the Fleet
57 Hand-steering room
58 Storerooms

A

C

B

ANTI-AIRCRAFT (AA) GUN AND MISSILE

A *Guided Missile*
1 Proximity fuse
2-3 Guidance and
control sections
4 Missile tail fins
5 Booster
6 Booster fins
7 Sustainer motor with
container for fuel
8 Missile wings
9 Warhead

B *Anti-aircraft gun
(Automatic)
(Bofors 40 mm mod/48)*
1 Flash reducer
2 Barrel
3 Cradle
4 Recoil brake
5 Gun balancing gear
6 Automatic loader

7 Rammer
8 Magazine
9 Elevating arc
10 Seat
11 Training and elevation
gear
12 Firing device
13 Platform
14 Mounting
15 Shield

C *Anti-aircraft
ammunition*
1 Projectile
2 Cartridge case, cartridge
1+2 Round (complete)
3 Loading clips
4 Percussion fuse,
nose fuse
5 Charge
6 Shell
7 Flare

A *Fulton's mine, the first moored mine*
1 Mechanical firing mechanism
2 Charge container
3 Wooden box

B *Mechanical mine (about 1830)*
1 Contact horn or button
2 Shell of mine
3 Anchor

C *Modern noncontrolled set-depth contact mine*
1 Mine horn
2 Shell of mine
3 Primer
4 Charge
5 Automatic disposal arrangement
6 Mooring cable (rope)
7 Anchor
8 Mooring cable drum
9 Pawling mechanism
10 Plummet wire drum
11 Plummet wire and plummet

D *Herz horn*
1 Horn cover
2 Lead horn
3 Electrolyte container
4 Electrodes

E *Depth-setting arrangement*
1 Mine before laying
2 Plummet falling
3 Length of plummet wire=set depth
4 Plummet bottoms, pawling locks cable drum
5 Moored mine

F *Antenna mine*
1 Ship's hull
2 Mine
3 Antenna buoy with copper points
4 Electrode
5 Lower antenna
6 Sea water acting as electrolyte

G *Pressure mine ("Oyster" mine), firing device*
1 Casing
2 Rubber bag
3 Diaphragm
4 Diaphragm contact
5 Adjustable contact
6 Leak hole

H *Magnetic (magnetic-acoustic) mine*
1 Variation of earth's magnetic field underneath ship with permanent magnetism
2 Variation of earth's magnetic field underneath degaussed ship
3 Variation of sound pressure
4 Induction coil
5 Charge
6 Primer with detonator
7 Safety device
8 Instrument box (with relay, ship counter, etc.)
9 Acoustic device
10 Parachute container

MINESWEEPING

A *Protector paravane*
1 Paravane
2 Towing line, serrated wire
3 Cutter
4 Swept mine

B *Wire sweep*
1 Minesweeper
2 Winch
3 Stern chock
4 Sweep wire
5 Kite wire
6 Snatch block
7 Kite, depressor
8 Serrated wire

C *Solenoid sweep*
1 Floating casing
2 Cable connection
3 Space for cable coil
4 Wood sheathing
5 Rudder
6 Acoustic hammer box
7 Cable

THE TORPEDO

A *Torpedo*
1 Horn
2 Primer
3 Explosive charge
4 Warhead
5 Air flask, air vessel
6 Fuel or water tank, destroyer torpedo: alcohol; submarine torpedo: water

7 Depth gear
8 Steam engine
9 Gyro-servomotor
10 Propeller shafts
11 Afterbody
12 Tail section
13 Air lever
14 Air charging valve
15 Fuel (water) charging valve

B *Pistol*
1 Safety propeller
2 Primer

C *Tail section*
1 Propeller shafts
2 Fins
3 Propellers
4 Steering rudder
5 Depth rudder

D *Torpedo net*
1 Swinging boom
2 Torpedo net

The torpedo net was an attempt to prevent damage from torpedo attacks

ANTI-SUBMARINE WEAPONS

A *Sonar (Asdics)*
 1 Frigate or destroyer
 2 Helicopter
 3 Asdic dome with
   transducer
 4 Asdic beam
 5 Sonar (Dipping Asdic)

B *Depth Charge (D/C)*
 1 Depth regulator
 2 Depth setting key
 3 Safety device

C *Anti-submarine (AS)*
 rocket
 1 Fuse, primer
 2 Fins

D *Anti-submarine (AS)*
 rocket launcher
 1 Barrel
 2 AS-rocket
 3 Training motor
 4 Flash shield
 5 Training gear
 6 Magazine

E *Same as D*
 (Four-tube launcher)

ACTION INFORMATION ORGANIZATION

A *Fire control radar*
1 Parabolic antenna
2 Radiator
3 Wave guide
4 Local stabilizer
5 Pedestal
6 Telescope

B *Predictor for ballistic data handling*

C *Range receiver*
1 Fine dial
2 Coarse dial

D *Principle of fire control*
1 Main director
2 Fire control radar
3 Range finder
4 Range+deflection+ elevation
5 Predictor
6-11 Data being handled in predictor
6 Wind direction and wind speed
7 Target's speed+ inclination
8 Own course and speed
9 Powder temperature
10 Barometic pressure and air temperature
11 Spotting corrections
12 Firing data (gun elevation and angle of training) to guns

E *Basic fire control principle*
1 Own course
2 Own ship
3 Deflection
4 Range
5 Inclination (angle on the target's bow)
6 Target
7 Target's course
8 Wind

F *Radar, range finders, etc.*
1 Fire control radar for main armament (surface)
2 Forward director control tower (DCT)
3 Range finder
4 Navigation radar
5 Air search (air warning) radar
6 Surface warning radar
7 Height finding radar
8 Fine control radar for close range armament
9 After main director with range finder and fire control radar
10 Aerials

WARSHIPS

1 Nelson's flagship at Trafalgar, *Victory*, built as early as 1765

2 Armored frigate of captain class

3 American frigate, about 1800

4 French ironclad *Jauréguiberry*, end of the 19th century

5 Swedish gunboat, 1870

6 John Ericssons' *Monitor*, 1862

7 The British protected cruiser, *Edgar*, end of the 19th century

WARSHIPS

8 French torpedo boat, 1890

9 French submarine, 1863

10 British battle cruiser, 1912

11 American destroyer, 1917

12 American battleship, 1912

13 German submarine, W.W. I

14 Swedish aircraft-carrying cruiser, 1936

WARSHIPS

15 German battleship, *Bismarck,* launched 1939

16 American escort vessel (frigate), W.W. II

17 German snorkel-fitted submarine, W.W. II, the snorkel is a watertight telescopic air intake, which makes it possible for the submarine to use its diesel engines when submerged

18 British motor torpedo boat (MTB), beginning of W.W. II

19 British minesweeper, end of W.W. II

20 Swedish destroyer, 1955

21 Modern Netherlands cruiser

WARSHIPS

22 British battleship, 1946
23 American aircraft carrier, 1947
24 American nuclear-powered submarine with 16 Polaris missiles
25 Modern Swedish motor torpedo boat
26 American nuclear-powered cruiser armed with guided missiles

An old engraving shows Magellan during his trip around the world, 1519—1522. Magellan was never able to complete this first circumnavigation of the globe himself, and of the original five vessels, with 265 men in the crew, only one ship, the VICTORIA; *and eighteen men returned. The engraving introduces the chapter on navigation and ship-handling.*

NAVIGATION AND SHIP-HANDLING

BY ROLF SCHEEN

The term navigation for this science is of comparatively recent date when compared with man's own hundreds-of-thousand-year history. Nobody knows when the first boat or the first ship was launched, but it is evident that the first man could not go very far from his original home without being stopped by water when he went out to look for something to eat. That water had to be spanned; the primitive craft is very, very old in the history of mankind. The first primitive navigation took place without an intended place of destination. The object was just to get over, to cross or pass a river, a bay, or a small lake. Of these first navigators, no man had ever been on the other side of a body of water. He only moved over the globe without knowing or thinking of a destination. Food was the only thing he thought of. He went in search of food; he crossed the water in order to get food. Only later, having left places where food was good and plentiful, he wanted to return, to find the same places once more. Then the question was to find one's way. Man learned to find out where he was. His primitive navigation must now be considered an art. The peoples of the Stone Age and of the Bronze Age might have been marvelously clever in many ways. But even if astronomy was considered a science in Babylon 3,800 years before our era and even if the Chinese were able to compute the advent of solar eclipses more than 4,000 years ago they were not able to transfer the results of astronomy to practical navigation at that time.

Rivers and coastal waters can be so turbid that even with a small boat it is impossible to see the bottom, if you have enough water to float the keel. Therefore, man from the oldest times has been forced to measure the depth of the water he was going to use. On ancient pictures of Egyptian riverboats a man can be seen in the fore part of the boat using a pole to determine depth and the advisability of continuing navigation. Very early, sailors or fishermen also learned to use lead and line to measure the depth when a pole could no longer be made use of. The lead was used on board the ship that was to take the Apostle Paul to Rome, the ship that foundered in the year 62. The lead was then so developed that it was already marked in fathoms. The main object of the lead was to save the ship from going aground. If the position of a shoal or bank had already been determined, other means were used to avoid it. Much used were (and are) the so-called landmarks. It is unnecessary to know all the ground, if you are to determine your position through landmarks and can follow a safe way through or past the dangerous places.

Very early, people who had learned to write were recording necessary information mostly, perhaps, for their own benefit. Greeks and Phoenicians collected what they could in so-called *peripli,* covering whole territories. Others misused this information. Herodotus (ca. 450 B.C.) relates that King Darius I of Persia about 490 B.C. hired Phoenician ships to spy upon the Greek coast in order to procure information about this country. Later on, sea charts became still more important than sailing directions. They could not be truly useful before the invention of the compass and they could never satisfy modern requirements until hydrographic offices had been established by the different nations to organize the work of surveying, sounding, etc.; but the chief of the famous library of Alexandria, Eratosthenes (276—196 B.C.) had already produced a map of the world with the first primitive framework of parallels and meridians.

A good chart should enable its user to draw the course (the compass direction) between two places. The charts on Mercator's projection were easily satisfactory in this respect. Gerard Mercator made the degrees of longitude parallel. As a result, he could draw a correct course line between two places on his chart, but the scale of the chart varied from the Equator toward the poles, so that at 60 degrees North, for instance, one nautical mile on the chart had twice the length of the mile at the Equator. In the neighborhood of the poles, the method could not be used at all.

As is well known, the distance from the Equator to the poles of the earth is divided in 90 degrees of latitude (north or south) for the purpose of ascertaining the position of a ship, for use on charts, for observations, etc. The Equator itself has been divided into 360 degrees of longitude, with verticals called meridians up to the poles. No 0-meridian being standard, different countries have used varius 0-meridians. At sea it was better to have a common 0-meridian for ships of all nations; consequently, many countries followed King Louis XIII's orders to place the 0-meridian through the Isle of Ferro. Ferro was thought to be the westernmost point of the Old World. From the year 1884, the 0-meridian through the Greenwich Observatory in England (founded 1675) may be considered international.

A great deal of courage was needed in ancient times to sail far out from the coast, losing all sight of land. No compass, no reliable charts existed. Good weather, the spirit of adventure, the feeling of having a good boat certainly tempted many to continue their explorations when prudence ought to have kept them back. As daring sea expeditions, the adventures of the old Norsemen through the mists of the North Atlantic to Iceland, Greenland, and North America must be said to rank high, but it must be presumed that they had quite a good knowledge of the celestial bodies and their movements in order to find their way to such distant countries and back again. Next to the sun, the Pole Star and perhaps still more the Little Dipper have helped navigators. For the Norsemen the brightest summer nights and also the Midnight Sun played a great part in their seamanship. Their ancient astronomical terms have been preserved, but their meaning has been difficult to explain, even in modern times. (For instance: *Eyktarstad*)

It has long been possible to determine latitude with a fair amount of certainty. But longitude was an almost insoluble problem so long as no instrument capable of measuring time with the necessary accuracy for use at sea had been invented. A chronometer was needed. Prizes were offered to anybody who could find the means of discovering the longitude. In 1714 the English Parliament granted 20,000 pounds for this purpose. Astronomers were able to determine the longitude by the help of lunar distances and other observations, but their methods were too impractical to be used at sea. At last, after working a whole lifetime, a Yorkshireman, John Harrison, in 1774, was given the prize for his invention. With Harrison, a revolution in the history of navigation had taken place; from now on the longitude of a ship's position at sea could be determined.

The most important innovation, however, was much older; this was the invention of the compass. No one knows who the inventor was. The Chinese Emperor Hoang-Ti is said to have used magnets on his chariot to find his way south as early as the third millennium B.C. But the earliest date for the use of a compass on board a ship occurs in Chinese literature in A.D. 1111, and it is possible that China had gotten the compass from India. According to Are Frode, the Norsemen are said to have used the *leidarstein* (loadstone or lodestone) for a primitive compass during a voyage to Iceland as early as in the year A.D. 868. Considering the huge quantities of magnetite to be found in Norway, it is not at all unreasonable to suppose that Norwegians very early conceived the idea of using magnetism on board their ships as they used it during their lives on shore. Their ability to find their way across the seas if they had no form of compass is almost incomprehensible.

Celestial navigation is based upon the measurement of the altitude of celestial bodies and the determination of their direction. All ships measuring the same celestial body at the same time and at the same altitude will be placed on the same astronomical position line. This can be determined according to principles first laid down by the American naval officer Thomas H. Summer in 1837, and further amplified by Marc St. Hilaire around 1875. Many different instruments have, in the course of time, been constructed for the measurement of the altitude of celestial bodies; the quadrant is said to have been invented by the Greek astronomer Hipparchos as early as the year 150 B.C. Levi ben Gerson from Catalonia discovered the Jacob's staff or the cross-staff in 1342; John Hadley constructed the Hadley quadrant in 1731; the British naval officer Campbell made the sextant in 1757.

To use celestial navigation it is necessary to have a number of tables computed in advance. Regimontanus published his *Ephemerides Astronomica* in 1475. Thomas Mayer at Göttingen edited the tables to be used in finding Greenwich time in 1755. The British Nautical Almanac, founded by the royal astronomer Nevil Maskeleyne and officially published since 1767, has proved its great value for the seafaring man using celestial navigation.

In modern times, especially after the Second World War, electronic navigation has become more and more important. Radio bearings were being experimentally used at the very beginning of the wireless era, in the 20th century. At present there are long-range radio navigational aids of the type called *Sonne* in German and *Consol* in English.

The Loran system, with the use of the so-called hyperbolic position line net systems, is based upon radio range finding instead of radio direction finding. The Decca system has much in common with the Loran, but transmits radio waves continually, not in interrupted signals as the Loran does. The position of a ship is determined by the phase difference between three waves received from three co-operating transmitters, which is measured and utilized together with a special Decca chart.

The simplest way of finding a course is naturally to steer directly to a goal, but that can only rarely be done. Sailing on the ocean, the course must be computed according to the latitude and the longitude and the longitude of the place of departure and of the destination. The magnetic compass has for many hundreds of years been used as the most convenient aid for finding one's way over the sea, but notice must be taken of the variation caused by the difference in position of the geographical North Pole from the magnetic North Pole. Consideration must also be taken of the amount of iron in the ship and her machinery, which will cause a deviation on the compass that will change with different courses and with different latitudes. This deviation is caused by magnetic forces on board the ship added to the magnetism of the earth.

In the 20th century magnetic compasses are more and more being replaced by gyrocompasses which are independent of magnetism and which, after a few small cor-

rections, will point directly toward the geographical North Pole. These gyrocompasses can easily be combined with gyrodials for taking bearings. They can also be combined with gyropilots for automatic steering of the ship.

Before the advent of charts, which give exact distances, it was, of course, very difficult to determine how far the ship had gone in a certain span of time. On rowing vessels some nations used to reckon the distance according to the time the rowers had been active (watches). Real distance, given in leagues, miles, etc., is, of course, much more exact. During the sailing ship era, the hand log and hourglass were used, but they could only give the speed at the time of logging. Nothing was recorded directly by the log as to the distance run. Later on, various kinds of patent logs were constructed to give the distance. They were towed after the ship and a special mechanism counted the number of miles run, which could be read directly on a dial on board the ship.

Thousands and thousands of foundered ships bear silent witness of the dangers of a vessel on her way from one port to another. Here, a very short summary will be given.

Invisible shoals. They are marked on the chart, if known. They are marked by beacons or lights, but these can be sunk or stray from their station, while the shoals represent permanent dangers. Darkness. Before lighthouses or lights were built along the coasts it was hardly possible to navigate at night. Even now, coastal navigation has its dangers; the coastal waters are perilous for a sailing ship or a powered vessel not under control, either of which could be thrown on a lee shore in a storm at any time of day. Lanterns are meant to help ships that pass at night, but too often they have been out of order.
Collisions. These happen too frequently. International rules of the road help to avoid them. Go slow, when necessary! Don't be afraid to stop! In modern times radar can be a help.
During wartime, mines, torpedoes, and other dangers are added to the usual perils of the sea. Degaussing or deperming will help against some mines. Convoys, camouflage, etc., have saved many ships from torpedoes.

A tragedy can come at any hour: fire, shipwreck, etc. Lifeboats and all kinds of lifesaving equipment must always be kept in perfect order, and all on board must know how to handle it. The use of distress signals must also be learned, so that you are always ready to tackle dangerous situations.

Engines have made maneuvering easier. Modern ships may have several rudders; and even a rudder in the fore part of the vessel; submarines must have horizontal rudders, called hydroplanes, for steering in the depths. The

hull is shaped so that the ship can turn very quickly. Engines can shift their vast power from one direction to another in seconds. However, wind, current, or breakdowns can destroy all these advantages. At the critical moment it is again man who must take over. He must do the real job; and he must know how to do it whether he is on a small picket boat or the commander of the mightiest ship in the world.

The term navigation, in modern times, is also used with airplanes. We talk about aerial navigation. Many of the problems for the ship and for the airplane are the same, but the far greater speed in the air and the height of the plane make navigation in the sky very different from navigation in the sea. That is still more so with the rocket. Rocket navigation, perhaps, uses the science of ballistics more than navigation, and it apparently has nothing to do with the old-time ship's navigation. After all, that may not be so correct. Ship navigation is so old and offers so much experience through the ages that it is difficult to think of anything really new that could happen in the art.

The revolution has come already, starting with a new base: electronic navigation. That revolution will continue, dictated by the needs of ships, airplanes, and rockets. Technical discoveries will also continue, as we strive for perfection.

The danger is that quick development will go beyond the conception of the ordinary human mind, until at last no one will be able to control our navigation.

For the sake of safety at sea, on land, and in the air, we must hope that man, the well-intentioned, thinking man, will always have the lead, will always be the controlling factor.

HAND LEAD AND LINE

The lead is the sailor's oldest navigational instrument, known even in ancient Egypt. It consists of a lead weight and a measured line, which is used to determine the depth of water. For different depths, leads of different weights were used, but today the deep-sea lead is replaced by sounding machines or echo sounders. The hand lead is still used occasionally in shallow water. The line used to be 20 fathoms long, and in the Royal British Navy it is marked in the following way:

2 fathoms: two strips of leather

3 fathoms: three strips of leather

5 fathoms: a piece of white duck

7 fathoms: a piece of red bunting

10 fathoms: a piece of leather with a hole in it

13 fathoms: a piece of blue serge

15 fathoms: a piece of white duck

17 fathoms: a piece of red bunting

20 fathoms: a piece of house line with two knots

THE LEAD

A *Egyptian boat model with oarsmen, helmsman, and leadsman (from a grave sediment, 2060-1730 B.C.)*

B, C *Deep-sea lead 16 to 20 lbs. The lower end of the lead, C2, is hollowed out, 3, to receive an arming of tallow on which samples of the sea bed are brought up for examination.*

D *Deep-sea lead of cast iron*

E *Sounding machine To make soundings possible without reducing the speed of the ship a sounding machine with a thin wire must be used*

1 Wire drum
2 Dial and pointer, indicating how many fathoms of wire have run out
3 Handle, to wind in the lead and also to act as a brake on the drum
4 Feeler which indicates when the lead has reached the bottom
5 Cylinder with glass sounding tubes
6 Sinker

7 Glass tube in brass guard. The tube is sealed at the upper end. The water entering the tube from the lower end compresses the air corresponding to the depth of water. By discoloring a mercury salt in the tube the water leaves a mark at the line of greatest compression and by this the depth of water is known.

F *Sound travels at a known speed through the water, and the echo sounder measures the time it takes for a transmitted sound to travel from the ship to the sea bed and return to the ship as an echo.*

1 Transmitter
2 Separate sound transmissions
3 Echoes of transmissions
4 Receiver
5 Oscillator in transmitter, 1
6 Reflector
7 Fresh water tank, welded to bottom plating
8 Recording unit

THE OLD LOG WITH A LINE AND GLASS

The chip log is an old instrument for measuring the speed of a ship. It consists of a flat piece of wood formed as a sector of a circle and weighted to enable it to float upright, secured to a line so as to *make it float square. When thrown overboard it will remain stationary in the water and, as the ship sails away, the measured line will reel off at a corresponding rate. An hourglass determines* *the fixed interval of time, and the length of line run out will measure the speed of the ship. A quick pull on the line will detach the peg in the log chip, making it float flat so it can be hauled in.*

1 The log, known as the wood float or chip
2 Lead pellets holding the chip vertically in the water

3 Wooden peg, which allows the chip to float flat when it is pulled out
4 Log-line measured off in "knots," having a similar relation to a nautical mile as the trickle of sand in the hourglass has to one hour

5 Log reel
6 Mark for two knots and a plain mark for half a knot
7 Hourglass, log glass, running for 28 seconds. A 14-second glass is used for speeds over 8 knots

THE LOG

A *Patent or taffrail log*
1 Rotator
2 Governor
3 Connecting log line
4 Fish and hook-and-eye fastenings
5 Register
6 Base plate

B *Pitometer log*
1 Indicator
2 Speedometer
3 Counter
4 Connection to log
5 Pitot tube
6 Low pressure tube to log
7 High pressure tube to log
8 Operating hand wheel for Pitot tube
9 Bottom plating
10 Top of double bottom
11 Static orifice
12 Dynamic orifice

C *Details of Chernikeeff log*
This is similar to the Pitometer log, but has a small fan called the impeller in the tube which extends from the ship's bottom. The rotation is electrically registered.
1 Impeller
2 Tube

A

B

C

D

OLD COMPASS CARDS

A *Compass, 13th century Reconstruction of a Scandinavian compass (leidarstein) with a bronze bowl and a wooden float, with a lodestone to point the compass*

1 Lid forming a cross with a center hole controlling the float
2 Float with lodestone
3 AUSTR, east
4 LANDSUDR, southeast
5 SUDR, south
6 UTSUDR, southwest
7 VESTR, west
8 UTNORDR, northwest
9 NORDR, north
10 LANDNORDR, northeast

B *Compass card, 1345*

C *Compass card, 1545*

D *Compass card, end of the 18th century*

COMPASSES

A *Pole compass*
   The laws of deviation were not fully understood in the early iron vessels; one way to get the compass out of the influence of the iron was to place the compass on a pole — often on a level so high that a ladder was needed to reach it

B *Compensating binnacle*
   Later, this deviation was compensated for by soft iron and permanent magnets in a binnacle
   1 Protecting hood with a pelorus mounted on top
   2 Quadrantal correctors
   3 Clinometer
   4 Paraffin oil lamps for emergency lighting
   5 Locker for permanent magnets

C *Liquid compass, sectional drawing*
   In most ship's compasses the compass card is immersed in a liquid which moderates its motion

D *Dry compass, sectional drawing*

E *The gyrocompass principle*
   1, 2, 3
   A pendulous gyro always adjusts its axis toward the North Pole
   3 A gyro axis pointing north
   4 The North Pole

F *Inside view of a gyrocompass*
   A gyrocompass is not influenced by deviation, but shows true north
   1 Rotor case
   2 Compensating weights
   3 Motor
   4 Bearings
   5 Compass card
   6 Repeater transmitter
   7 Correcter for speed and latitude

G *Gyro-repeater compass*

OLD NAVIGATIONAL INSTRUMENTS

A Astrolabe, constructed by the Arabs in the 10th century, and used, mostly by the Spaniards and Portuguese, up to the 17th century. It consists of a freely suspended graduated ring with a diametrical ruler holding two sight vanes through which the sun or a star may be observed, the altitude being read off on the circle.

B The fore staff is composed of a square staff and three vanes of different lengths. The sides of the staff have different scales, each corresponding to one of the vanes. When observing the altitude of the sun (star) only one vane is used. Holding one end of the staff to his eye, the observer moves the vane until he sees its lower end level with the horizon and the upper end in one with the sun. The altitude is read off where the vane cuts the staff.

C Davis' quadrant is composed of two arcs of a circle having the same center and three vanes: the horizon vane (1) with a slot, the shade vane (2), and the sight vane (3) with a sight hole. The horizon vane is fixed at the center, the other two vanes run upon the arcs. The quadrant is used with the observer's back to the sun. The shade vane is set at a suitable number of degrees, and the observer moves the sight vane until he observes the sun's shadow in one with the horizon, as seen through the slot in the horizon vane.

D Gunter's quadrant is made on the same principles as the Davis' quadrant, and it is used with the observer's back to the sun.

E Hadley's octant, invented in 1731, and a forerunner of the sextant. The octant brought the art of measuring altitudes at sea to theoretical perfection, and later improvements are due to better methods of manufacturing only.

A MODERN SEXTANT

The sextant is an improvement on Hadley's octant, which is said to have been invented in 1731. The sextant is a portable, reflecting astronomical instrument for measuring angles. When used, it can be held in the hand without a stand, which is essential on board ships at sea. The instrument consists of a sector-shaped frame with a graduated arc of a circle. Pivoted at the center of the arc is a radius bar, which swings across the surface of the graduated arc. The principal parts of a sextant are:

1 The frame
2 The arc, known as the limb
3 The index bar
4 Clamping mechanism
5 Micrometer screw
6 Index mirror
7 Horizon glass
8 Telescope
9 Index shades
10 Horizon shades
11 Measured angle
12 Reading of measured angle, here 45° O'

BEARINGS

A *Reconstruction of a compass card from the Viking Age*

B *Pelorus*
1, 2 Sight vanes
3 Position line
4 Object
5 Fore-and-aft mark to which the ship's course on the pelorus is clamped
6 Compass bearing

C *Cross bearing*
The exact position of the ship (1) will be known if bearings of two objects (2 and 3) are taken at the same time

D *Distance by four-point bearing*
When a fixed object (2) is bearing 45 degrees on the bow (3) note the time or log. Then the same course is steered until the object bears on the beam, or 90 degrees from the course (4). The distance (6) run by the ship (1) in the interval is the distance (7) of the object when abeam. This is clear from the fact that the ship's course and the two bearings form an isosceles triangle (3, 4, 5), where the two sides (6, 7) are equal.

A *With the aid of a rotatable aerial in the form of a loop or frame the bearing to a radio station may be fixed*

B *The theory*

1 Radio station sending

2 When the frame aerial is facing the direction of the station the incoming signal is not audible

3 When the frame aerial is edge on to the direction of the transmitting station, the signal strength is reaching its maximum

C *How to take a bearing*
With the loop aerial in the position of B 2, there is a well-defined silence arc of a few degrees on each side of the required direction. By rotating the frame either way the signal rises to audibility, and by reading off on the scale the two points limiting the arc of silence the midpoint between gives the direction of the transmitting station. If the frame is at B 3 and is turned 10 degrees, it makes no difference in the sound. Graphically it is as radius 4 projected on radius 5 to radius 5, or as Cos 10° to 1. In the position B 2 the difference in sound is quite audible, like the line C 2 compared with 0 or utter silence.

D *Cross bearing*
The wireless bearings are generally taken as cross bearings in the same manner as optical bearings. Sectors of 30° near the coastline should be avoided, as the bearings are unreliable in that zone.

E *Fixed loops*
Modern installations may have two fixed loops at right angles to one another. By a system of coils the same result is obtained as when a turnable frame aerial is used.

F *Direction finder operating panel*

G *Because of the deviation influence of the hull, the incoming radio wave will deviate · from the true direction (1). A table of radio deviation may look like G 2. The deviation is relative to the ship's head only.*

RADIO NAVIGATION: DECCA, LORAN, ETC.

By sending radio waves at exactly the same moment from two stations and by measuring the intervals between their arrival at a ship it is possible to fix a line on which the ship must be located. If the two pulses arrive at the same time, this line is the normal median line between the two stations. But if there is a difference in time, the line is a hyperbola. By measuring the difference in time between two pairs of stations, each pair giving a hyperbola, the ship must be on their intersection.

Special charts with these hyperbolas printed in red, green, and purple are used with the Decca system. The receiving unit registers the difference in time automatically and shows it as hyperbola numbers on three dials. Each Decca chain consists of one master station which together with three slave stations forms three pairs of senders. Each pair is represented in the Decca chart by a system of hyperbolas of its own color. On the red and green dials in the figure above it is possible to determine on which hyperbola the ship is positioned at the moment of observation.

In the Loran system the difference in time between the two sending stations is shown on a cathode ray tube, as illustrated to the right in the figure above. The left circle shows no difference between the pulses, and so the ship must be on the normal median line between the two stations. The right-hand picture indicates a difference in time, which means that the ship is on a hyperbola which is then determined in the same way as in the Decca system.

RADAR (page 237)

A *Principles of radar*
A scanner (1) sends out high-frequency radio pulses in a beam (2), which is very narrow in the horizontal plane. The beam sweeps around the horizon through the rotation of the scanner. The radio pulses are fed to the scanner through a wave guide (3). The target (4), which is hit by the beam, reflects part of it (5) back to the scanner, and through the wave guide the echo signal goes to the T.R. unit (6). Here, the signal is transformed so that the P.P.I. (7), which is the Plan Position Indicator, can give a picture

Continued

signal. On the P.P.I. tube's screen (8) a line appears at the center signal. On the P.P.I. tube's screen (8) a line to the edge of the tube and in the same direction as that in which the scanner is pointing. The light intensity on the line is strengthened by the target's echo signal, and in this way marks the target on the screen. The bearing is given by the direction of the line from the center of the screen, and the target's range by the distance of the echo from the center of the screen.

9 Voltage regulator or stabilizer

10 Motor generator

B *6-foot scanner*

C *Slotted wave guide scanner*

D *True motion radar*

1 Radar on/off

2 Scanner on/off

3 Standby/transmit

4 Tuning

5 Gain

6 Anti-clutter sea

7 Tx/Rx monitor on/off

8 Power monitor on/off

9 Pulse length

10 Hand speed control

11 Speed input selection

12 N/S and E/W re-sets

13 Re-set

14 Log flasher

15 Course-made-good control

16 Compass repeater

17 Presentation switch

18 Relative motion warning

19 Focus

20 Tube brilliance

21 Anti-clutter rain control (variable F.T.C or differentiation)

22 Shift control

23 Illumination dimmers

24 Range scale switch

25 Range scale and range ring interval indicator

26 Range ring brilliance control

27 Range marker brilliance control

28 Interscan and variable range marker range scale

29 Bearing cursor control

30 Bearing and range measurement scales

31 Heading marker control

32 Coarse and fine ranging controls

LIGHTHOUSES

A Open coal fire at Djur-
sten, Sweden, 1765

B Fire on tilting spar,
1635

C Modern caisson light-
house, built of concrete
on shore, launched, and
towed to its station and
there sunk

D Pharos at Alexandria,
300 B.C.

E Torre de Herculum at
Coruna, at the time of
Christ

F Tour d'Ordre at Bou-
logne, A.D. 40

G Cordouan at the mouth
of Girande estuary in
France, 1610

H Eddystone light in the
Channel

1 1698 (at low water)

2 1759 (at low water)

3 1882 (at high water)

LIGHTHOUSE LAMPS

A *Lighthouse lamp for paraffin oil with 4 wicks, 1880's*

B *Lens arrangement with Fresnel's lenses and prisms, about 6 feet diameter; 500,000 Heffner lights*

C *Light buoy*
1 Lamp burning acetylene gas
2 Sun valve, which puts the light out in daytime and thus reduces the consumption of gas by 50%

   (1 and 2 are shown in detail in D)

3 Radar reflector
4 Whistle
5 Mooring chain
6 Anti-rotating fin
7 Ballast

D *Lamp and sun valve*
1 Sun valve
2 Fresnel lens

SOME IMPORTANT LIGHTHOUSES

None of the lighthouses included here has a visibility of less than 20 nautical miles. Almost 1,000 lights with a visibility of 20 nautical miles and up exist. In *regions where there are a great many bright lights it has been necessary to extend the limits so that, for example, all Japanese* *lights marked on the map have a visibility exceeding 30 nautical miles. The visibility in nautical miles is indicated parenthetically.*

1 Makapuu Point, Oahu (27)
2 Molokai (28)
3 Cape Hinchinbrook (22)
4 Cape St. James, Queen Charlotte Islands (24)
5 Main Channel (22)
6 Cape Blanco (22)
7 Cape Mendocino (28)
8 Farallon, San Francisco (26)
9 Point Sur (23)
10 Anacapa Island (23)
11 West Benito Island (28)
12 Natividad Island (26)
13 Cape Tosco (23)
14 Guaymas, Cape Haro (24)
15 Cerro Partido (24)
16 Mazatlán (30)
17 Punta de Campos (26)
18 Acapulco, Grifo Island (26)
19 Golfito (24)

20 Santa Elena Point (25)
21 Callao (25)
22 Atico Point (21)
23 Curaumilla Point (24)
24 Guafo Island (28)
25 New Year's Islands, Staten Island (20)
26 Cape Virgins (21)
27 Leones Isle (23)
28 Montevideo (29)
29 Arvoredo Islet (24)
30 Castelhanos Point (27)
31 Cape Frio (28)
32 Cape Agostinho (24)
33 Olinda Point (24)
34 Mel Point (24)
35 Chacachacare Islet, Trinidad (30)
36 El Roque (23)
37 Cartagena (26)
38 Manzanillo Point (24)
39 Bocas del Toro (23)
40 Port Cortez (23)

41 Roca Partida (23)
42 Cape Moul à Chique, St. Lucia (35)
43 La Trinité Bay, Martinique (27)
44 Hams Bluff, St. Croix (27)
45 Cape Borinquén (24)
46 Guantánamo (26)
47 Pensacola (20)
48 St. Augustine (20)
49 Gibb's Hill, Bermuda (26)
50 Cape Hatteras (20)
51 Cape Charles (20)
52 Chapel Hill Beacon (21)
53 Staten Island (21)
54 Cape Cod (20)
55 Seguin Island (20)
56 Cape Gaspé (26)
57 Cape Pine (40)
58 Belle Isle (28)
59 Dyrholaey (27)
60 Myggenaes (22)

61 Sumburgh Head, Shetland Islands (24)
62 Dunnet Head (24)
63 Whitby (22)
64 South Foreland (26)
65 Lizard (21)
66 Great Ormes Head (24)
67 St. Bees (25)
68 Mull of Galloway (25)
69 Barra Head (33)
70 Flannan Islands, Hebrides (24)
71 Cape Wrath (27)
72 Clare Islands (25)
73 Bull Rock (23)
74 Mine Head (23)
75 Cape Stolbiovo (20)
76 Kharlov Island (27)
77 Vardöy (22)
78 Udsire (22)
79 Kullen (24)
80 Hogland (26)
81 Dager Ort, Kopu (25)
82 Dornbusch (24)

83 Stevns Klint (21)
84 Hirtshals (20)
85 Helgoland (24)
86 Hook of Schouwen (41)
87 Cape Gris-Nez (21)
88 Cape La Heve (27)
89 Ouessant (20)
90 Biarritz (22)
91 Hercules Tower, Coruña (25)
92 Cape Finisterre (29)
93 Cape Roca (30)
94 Cape St. Vincent (22)
95 Mesa de Roldán (31)

96 Cape Nao (27)
97 Cape Formentor, Mallorca (30)
98 Cape San Sebastián (31)
99 Cape Camarat (28)
100 Punta del Faro (27)
101 Cape Pertusato (25)
102 Cape Sandalo (28)
103 Imperatore Point, Ischia (31)
104 Milazzo (24)
105 Cape Santa Maria di Leuca (25)
106 Sapientza (25)

CHARTS

Verbal descriptions have probably existed as long as man has sailed. The oldest written "pilots" are the Greek Periples which gave distances and courses (about 300 B.C.). These were the origins of the Roman Portulanes. In the 15th and 16th centuries "pilots" were published in most West European countries.

A The depths off the Norwegian coast are described by Olaus Magnus, in 1555, as being bottomless.

B The title page of the Dutch "Het Leeskaartboek van Wisboy" (the "Chart book" from Visby), first published in 1551. Several editions followed in Dutch as well as in German. The book also contained woodcut shore views. This figure is from the edition of 1561.

C Native chart of the Marshall Islands consisting of a framework of palmleaf veins with shells or coral pieces indicating the different islands and their relative positions. The distances between the islands were not always known, but most important were the directions.

D Shore view showing transit marks, etc., on a modern chart or in a pilot.

CHARTS AND SURVEYING

A *Detail from a Swedish chart of the Baltic, 1645*

B *A Swedish chart of the Sound, 1819; the same region is shown in the upper part of A*

C *Coast survey chart, beginning of the 19th century*

D *"Running survey," a common British method to plot the shore line*

E *Swedish surveying vessel, Gustaf af Klint*

THEORY OF SAILING

A *A boat beating to windward*
1 Sail
2 The force and direction of the wind, which can be resolved into the two components, 3 and 4
3 This force blowing parallel to the sail may be disregarded
4 This force can be resolved into two components, 5 and 6

5 This force works abeam and tends to heel the boat and to drive it to leeward. This tendency, however, is largely overcome by the lateral resistance of the water on the boat's hull and keel.
6 Of the original wind force, it is this component only that carries the boat ahead

B *Reaching; the wind abeam*
1 When the wind is abeam the lateral component (1) is reduced and the fore and aft component (2) is increased. The boat moves faster than when beating to windward (A).

C *Running*
   When running, the sails must not be at right angles to the direction of the wind
1 Mainsail
2 Spinnaker
D *Center of effort*
   Every sail has a center of effort (1). The center of effort of the total sail area (2) is obtained by combining the centers of each sail. Theoretically, if the center

of effort is ahead of the center of lateral resistance (3), the boat will tend to pay off from the wind. If 2 is abaft 3, the boat will tend to come up into the wind.
   In reality, the boat, when sailing, is heeling to leeward and the force of the wind will be applied at the center of effort on the lee side of the boat and cause her

to luff. To counteract this, the center of effort of the sails is always placed forward of the center of lateral resistance, as shown above.

E *A fact which is not familiar to everyone is that a drop keel under special circumstances may have a dangerous capsizing effect, for instance, if the boat when running suddenly broaches to.*

THE SET OF SAILS

A *A square-rigged vessel beating to windward*
In a square-rigger sailing on the wind the lower yards are always braced up more than the upper yards. The reason for this is that the lower sails cannot be set as flat as the upper sails, and thus require a broader wind to fill them than the small sails. Again, should the wind shift and the ship be caught aback, the upper sails will back first and warn the ship in time so that she can be paid off.

B *The lead of the fore staysail sheet*
1 There must be sufficient gap between the fore staysail and the mainsail, otherwise (as in the figure) the driving force of the mainsail will be reduced

2 A fore staysail which is correctly sheeted increases the suction on the lee side of the mainsail and thus increases its power

C *Unsteady wind*
A squall generally blows in a fan-shaped pattern. In spite of paying-off at the beginning and then luffing, the squall may be used to bring the boat to windward of her first track.

A BARK SAILING ON DIFFERENT COURSES

1 Bark sailing on the wind on the starboard tack

2 Sailing, reaching with wind abeam on the starboard side

3 Going large with the wind abaft the beam on the starboard side

4 Running free with the wind on the starboard quarter

5 Running before the wind; the wind is on the starboard side; headsails are partly blanketed, some staysails are furled

6 Running dead before the wind, scudding in a gale; spanker is furled, staysails not drawing, the headsails are blanketed

7 Running before the wind; wind is on the port side. Headsails are partly blanketed, some staysails are furled

8 Running free with the wind on the port quarter

9 Going large, sailing with a fair wind, with the wind abaft the beam on the port side

10 Sailing, reaching with the wind abeam on the port side

11 Sailing on the wind on the port tack

SMALL BOAT HANDLING

A *To fetch a buoy*
1 Sails set to the wind
2 Luff and trim sails to the wind
3 Luff and flatten in the sails
4 Luff as much as possible and spill the wind from the foresail and mainsail
5 Steer close to windward of the buoy and carefully judge the speed of approach

B *Going about*
1 Keep her full and by
2 "Helm's alee"
3 Flatten the foresail (applicable to dull-turning boats only)
4 Haul the foresail over and trim sheets by the wind on the new tack

C *Jibing*
1 Boat steering before the wind; you want to take the wind on the port quarter
2 Luff a little and shorten your sheets
3 By ready to jibe
4 Up helm; jibe easily and let the sheets run
5 Meet her and trim yaw sails

D *Yawing influence of right-hand propeller going astern;*
the blades of the screw have a better grip in the water at the deepest part of the rotation, and work the stern to port

E *Going alongside, port side to the quay*
1 Approach the quay at a broad angle
2 Stop
3 Full astern
4 Stop

F *Starboard side to the quay*
1 Small angle to pier; stop
2 Slow astern
3 Port helm
4 Stop

A SQUARE-RIGGED VESSEL, A THREE-MASTED BARK, WEARING

1 The bark is sailing on the wind on the starboard tack.

2 "Ready to wear ship!" The mainsail is clewed up and the braces are coiled down for running.

3 The spanker is furled. "Up helm!" "Square in the mainyard!" The wheel is put to port and the mainyard is squared.

4 Without sail aft the vessel is paying off.

5 The bark is before the wind. "Round forward!" The headsails are braced around and the jibs sheeted over to starboard.

6 When she is coming up on the new tack the headsails will meet her. The after yards are braced up.

7 The spanker is set and all sails are trimmed by the wind.

8 The bark is kept on the wind on the port tack. The main sail is set and the deck cleared up.

A SQUARE-RIGGED VESSEL, A THREE-MASTED BARK, TACKING

1 The bark is sailing on the wind on the port tack. "Ready about!"

2 She is kept off a little to make all sails draw better to increase the speed.

3 "Helm's alee!" The wheel is put down, the headsheets are let go to make the jibs spill the wind; the spanker is hauled aweather to assist the luffing.

4 The bark is nearly into the wind. Now "Mainsail haul!" The mainyards are braced around, the jibs are hauled over and sheeted home, while the vessel is head in the wind.

5 The movement ahead is decreasing. With the headsails aback the bark is forced over to port.

6 When the sails of the mainmast begin to fill, the order is, "Let go and haul!" and the headsails are hauled around.

7 The vessel is paying off until the sails are filling. All sails are trimmed by the wind.

8 The bark is going ahead, the wake is becoming normal.

9 She is kept on the wind on the starboard tack; the running gear is coiled down.

A SAILING VESSEL, A BRIG, BACKING AND FILLING DOWN A RIVER WITH THE EBB TIDE, AGAINST A HEADWIND. SHE HAS ONLY THE TOPSAILS SET.

1 The brig is filling both topsails to make her move ahead to keep her in the fairway

2 Backing the mainyard stops her progress and makes her drift broadside downriver

3 Backing all makes her take a stern board

4 By pointing the yards into the wind she is made to stand still and drift with the ebb tide

5 Filling the fore topsail makes her draw ahead

6 Filling all makes her go ahead more

7 She is kept off a little to increase her movement through the water

8 She is making sail, and trims them by the wind

9 She is clear of the river and stands to sea under all sail on the starboard tack

10 Wind direction

11 The ebb tide

TO HEAVE TO AND TO GOOSE-WING A SAIL

When a sailing ship was in a contrary gale of wind the order to heave to meant that most of the sails were taken in and the helm was put down. This kept the ship's head to the wind, and, with the sea on the bow, she would ride

well enough as long as some sail could be carried. This full-rigged ship has the fore topmast staysail, the mizzen staysail and the goose-winged main lower topsail set. To furl the weather half of a lower topsail was the last re-

source to shorten sail without having to furl all and drift under bare poles. The large scale drawing shows a part of the main mast with the goose-winged lower topsail. The numbers indicate:

1 Main mast
2 Heel of topmast
3 Mainyard with mainsail furled
4 Upper topsail yard with topsail furled
5 Lower topsail yard
6 Goose-winged lower topsail

7 Heavy lashing on sail, parceled to protect sail from chafe
8 Size of lower topsail when set
9 Lower topsail bunt-lines
10 Lower topsail clew-lines

MANEUVERING A POWERED SHIP WITH A RIGHT-HANDED SINGLE SCREW   *(Page 253)*

A *Turning with the wind ahead*
1 Ahead with the rudder hard astarboard
2 Full astern with the rudder hard aport
3 Ahead with starboard rudder
4 Steady the helm on the new course

B *Turning with the wind astern*
1 Ahead with the rudder astarboard
2 Full astern with starboard rudder
3 Before getting sternway: Full ahead with starboard rudder and the screw effect will help swing the ship
4 Steady on the new course

C *Turning with the wind on the quarter*
1 Astern with the rudder hard astarboard
2 Full ahead with port rudder; steady the helm on the new course

A *The effect of the rudder*
1 When turning, the power of the rudder may be dissolved into two components: one braking the ship and one forcing the stern aside

2 When the ship starts turning, a resistance arises on the bow which co-operates with the rudder
3 Only after several ship's lengths will the stern pass the original track

B *Heeling during a turn*
1 At first, the ship is heeled inward. This depends upon the fact that the rudder component and the lateral resistance work on different levels. Then, the centrifugal power applied at the center of gravity makes the ship list outward.

MANEUVERING A POWERED SHIP

C *Going alongside*
1 Put a spring ashore, slow ahead, starboard the rudder
2 When in position, tie her up, finish with engines

D *Leaving the quay*
1, 2 Keep a spring ashore, go slow ahead, and port your rudder
3 Let go the spring, slow astern, rudder amidships

E *Leaving the quay turning*
1 Keep a spring ashore, go slow ahead, and port your rudder
2 Stop engine, rudder amidships, shift the spring, further astern
3 Heave away the spring, go slow astern, starboard rudder
4 Let go the spring, go slow ahead, port your rudder

F *Leaving the quay under different current circumstances*
1 The ship has the current from ahead and the starboard side to the quay. Hold on to the spring aft and ease off the forward breast rope. The vessel is held parallel with the quay by engine and rudder.

2 The ship has the port side to the quay and the tidal stream aft (right-handed screw), the forward spring is held on and she is eased off by the breast rope aft. When all clear, slow astern and let go the shore lines.

3 If the ship has the current aft port side to quay, and left-handed propeller (or starboard side to quay, right-handed propeller), the forward spring is held on, and the aft breast rope is eased off. Then the breast rope is held on while the engine is put slow astern, with the rudder to port (starboard).

MOORING AND BELAYING

A *Bitts*
B *Knightheads*
C *Bitts on the forecastle head*

D *Knighthead*
   A-D are from a book on ship building by Å.C. Rålamb (1691)

E *Belaying to a single bollard*
F *Belaying to twin bollards*
   1 Racked turns

G *Stoppering a rope*
   Stoppers are used when hawsers are to be moved from the winch to the bollards, chain stoppers are used on wires

H *Two berthing hawsers on the same bollard on shore*
   1 Wrong way, the second hawser will block the first one
   2 Right way, either of the hawsers can be removed from the bollard independently of the other

I *Berthing hawsers*
   1 Stern rope
   2 After breast rope
   3 After back spring
   4 Fore back spring
   5 Fore breast rope
   6 Head rope

AUXILIARY VESSELS

1 Dutch pilot cutter,
1880's
2 Old Swedish sailing
pilot cutter

3 New York pilot
schooner
4 Modern pilot vessel
5 Modern pilot staysail
schooner, United States
west coast

6 Old pulling lifeboat
7 English sailing lifeboat,
about 1900
8 Norwegian cruising
lifeboat, *Colin Archer*,
built 1893

9 Modern British self-
righting lifeboat
10 Modern Swedish cruis-
ing lifeboat

AUXILIARY VESSELS

11 Ocean-going tug
12 Harbor tug
13 Floating drydock
14 Cable ship

TONGUE

AUXILIARY VESSELS

15 Russian ice breaker, *Ermak,* built in 1899
16 Modern ice breaker, displacement about 5,000 tons with diesel electrical machinery
17 Light ship
18 Salvage vessel
19 Bucket dredger
20 Training ship, *Denmark,* three-masted full-rigged ship

SAILOR'S OUTFIT

A *Seaman's chest with tassel work on its canvas-covered lid*
2 *End view of chest*
3 *Fancy handle*

B *Sailor's canvas bag (3 ft. high), made of five half cloths*
2 *The bottom of the bag with its canvas handle, 3*
4 *The shackle of the bag with bolt and lock*

C *Shetland wool jersey*
D *Sou'wester*

E *Sailor's sheath knife, carried in the middle of the back where it was available to both hands*

F *A young sailor from the 1860's*

G *An old sailor from the 1860's*

EQUIPMENT

1 Water jar (4 ft. high), from a Swedish East Indiaman, 18th century
2 Medicine chest, 19th century
3 Rum keg
4 Earthenware jug for wine or vinegar

PROVISIONS

Today, food on board ships is the same as that on shore. By freezing and other methods of preservation it is possible to keep fresh food even on long voyages. Formerly, however, things were different. Preserved food was scarce and voyages took a longer time.

1 Harness cask for salted beef and pork
2 A canvas bag used to hang meat in the rigging may be seen even in our day

3 Ship biscuits
4 To prevent scurvy, lime juice was used

5 When the Frenchman F. Appert invented the canning method in 1804 the problem of food supply on board ships began to be solved. The most common canned products on board were corned beef and condensed milk.

6 Dried fish, a common food on board

7, 8 On long voyages sailing ships carried some livestock for fresh provisions. In good weather, chickens would thrive and lay eggs for the cabin table. Pigs could stand all kinds of weather at sea, and a few were always carried on deep-water voyages.

SAILOR'S HOBBIES

1 Ship model in bottle
2 Circular mat, plaited of three parts
3 Three-stranded Turk's head

4 Cross made on board, and used as cabin-altar during W.W. II

5 Bottle engraved with a nail by two Danish sailors on board the sloop *3 Bröder* (*3 Brothers*)

6 Carved wooden box
7 Tool bag of canvas with strap of sennit
8 Plaited cot strap

*This picture of a rope-
yard is taken from the
classic nautical volume
Allgemeines Wörterbuch
der Marine by J.H.
Röding, published in
1798.*

Fore lower topgallant sail 100, 101, 103
Fore lower topgallant brace 108
Fore lower topgallant buntline 108
Fore lower topgallant clewline 108
Fore lower topgallant sail 100, 101, 103
Fore lower topgallant sheet 108
Fore lower topgallant yard 72, 73
Fore lower topsail 100, 101, 102, 103
Fore lower topsail brace 108
Fore lower topsail buntline 108
Fore lower topsail clewline 108
Fore lower topsail sheet 108
Fore lower topsail yard 72, 73
Foremast 20, 21, 25, 32, 33, 74, 75, 77, 80, 81, 87, 92, 93, 110, 115, 133
Foremast head 115
Forenede Dampskibsel-skab, Det 137
Fore peak 115, 116
Fore peak bulkhead 36
Fore peak halliard 115, 116
Fore peak hatch 60
Fore peak tank 36
Fore rigging 80, 87
Fore royal 100, 101, 102
Fore royal backstay 80
Fore royal brace 108
Fore royal buntline 108
Fore royal clewline 108
Fore royal mast 72, 73, 80
Fore royal pole 72, 73
Fore royal sheet 108
Fore royal stay 80, 86, 88, 89
Fore royal staysail 119
Fore royal staysail downhaul 119
Fore royal staysail halliard 119
Fore royal staysail sheet 119
Fore royal yard 72, 73
Fore sail 87, 92, 100, 101, 102, 103, 110, 120, 198, 247
Fore sail sheet 92
Fore sheet 87, 108, 116
Fore shroud 80
Forestay 80, 86, 87, 88, 89, 92, 115

Forestay lanyard 87
Fore staysail 92, 102, 103, 115, 245
Fore staysail halliard 115
Fore staysail sheet 118
Fore steaming light 65
Fore tack 87, 108
Fore tack bumpkin 87
Fore throat 115, 116
Fore throat halliard 115, 116
Fore top 72, 73
Fore topgallant backstay 80
Fore topgallant bowline 87
Fore topgallant mast 72, 73, 80, 92
Fore topgallant rigging 80
Fore topgallant sail 102
Fore topgallant stay 80, 86, 87, 88, 89
Fore topping lift 116
Fore topmast 72, 73, 80, 92
Fore topmast backstay 80
Fore topmast cap backstay 80
Fore topmast crosstree 72, 73
Fore topmast preventer stay 86
Fore topmast rigging 80
Fore topmast stay 80, 86, 87, 88, 89, 92
Fore topmast staysail 88, 89, 92, 100, 101, 102, 103, 119, 251
Fore topmast staysail downhaul 87, 88, 89, 119
Fore topmast staysail halliard 119
Fore topmast staysail sheet 88, 89, 119
Fore topmast staysail tack 86, 88, 89
Fore topsail 87, 102
Fore topsail bowline 86, 87
Fore topsail brace 90
Fore trysail 103
Fore upper topgallant brace 108
Fore upper topgallant buntline 108
Fore upper topgallant downhaul 108
Fore upper topgallant sail 100, 101
Fore upper topgallant sheet 108
Fore upper topgallant yard 72, 73
Fore upper topsail 100, 101, 102, 103
Fore upper topsail brace 108

Fore upper topsail buntline 108
Fore upper topsail downhaul 108
Fore upper topsail sheet 108
Fore upper topsail yard 72, 73
Fore vang 92
Fore yard 72, 73, 75, 77, 87, 92, 110
Forward bitt 33
Form 19
Formosa 134
Forward director control tower 217
Forward elevation 36
Forward oil pan 166
Forward perpendicular 24
Forward turbocharger 166
Foundation 58, 151, 157
4 (signal flag) 137
Four-by-three tackle 123
Four-fold tackle 123
Four-letter signal 139
Four-masted bark 72, 73, 74, 76, 77, 80, 100, 101, 108, 116, 130, 131
Four-masted barkentine 103, 130, 131
Four-masted fore-and-aft schooner 74, 102, 132, 133
Four-masted full-rigged ship 74
Four-masted jackass bark 130, 131
Four-masted ship 102, 130, 131
Four-masted topsail schooner 130, 131
Four-point bearing 234
Fourth Substitute (signal flag) 137
Four-tube launcher 216
Frame 26, 27, 28, 30, 36, 38, 39, 44, 45, 199, 233, 235
Frameless double-ender 18
Frame lines 22, 23
Framework 18
Framing 18, 31, 37, 45
France, flag 134
France 165
Frapping ring 63
Freeboard 53
Freeing port 31
Freighter 164
French Grand Bank schooner 173
French lugger 173

French motor trawler 173
French tunny yawl 175
Fresh water pump 107
Fresh water summer loadline 52
Fresh water summer timber loadline 52
Fresh water tank 227
Fresh water tropical loadline 52
Fresh water tropical timber loadline 52
Fresnel lens 64, 239
Frigate 32, 40, 86, 216, 218, 219, 220, 221
Front header, boiler 156
Front plate, boiler 152
Front tube plate, boiler 154
Fruit carrier 164
Fuel charging valve 215
Fuel injection pump 166, 167
Fuel oil tank 167
Fuel pipe 167
Fuel pump 167
Fuel tank 215
Fuel valve 166, 167
Full astern 247
Full line 19
Full-rigged four-masted ship 102
Full-rigged ship 74, 76, 77, 102, 251, 257
Full speed astern 138
Full dimensioned ship 53
Fulton, Robert 150, 160
Fulton's mine 213
Funnel 49, 61, 150, 152, 154, 167, 207
Funnel cape 154
Furl 248, 251
Furnace 152, 156, 157
Furnace bar 152, 156
Furnace bridge 152, 156
Furnace door 152, 156
Furnace front 152
Furnace grate 156
Furnace peephole 157
Furnace tube 157
Furness Lines 49
Futtock 26, 27
Futtock rigging 81
Futtock shrouds 81, 83, 90, 91, 110
Fuse 209, 212, 216

G

G (signal flag) 138
Gaff 72, 73, 92, 114, 115, 116, 117, 136
Gaff band 123
Gaff-rigged cutter 132, 133

Gaff sail 99, 114, 115, 116, 117
Gaff topsail 92, 100, 101, 103, 117
Galleass 18
Galleon 18, 126
Galley 18, 22, 23, 32, 61, 148, 199, 210, 211
Galley funnel 61
Galley oar 148
Galley stove 61
Galley wood 32
Galliot 18
Gallows 26
Galvanized-steel strand 141
Gammoning 86, 87
Garboard strake 20, 21, 27, 30, 154
Garnet 107
Gas boiler 167
Gasket 86, 104, 113, 191
Gas turbine outlet to boiler, diesel engine 166
Gauge board, diesel engine 166
Gauge glass 152
Gävle 139
Gear 47, 55, 106, 109, 119, 150, 157, 159, 167, 196, 212, 215, 216
Gear housing 58, 201
Gearing, reduction 210, 211
Generator 167, 210, 211, 237
Genoa (jib sail) 198
German heur boat 173
German motor trawler 174
German North Sea ketch 173
Gibb's Hill (lighthouse) 240
Gig 132, 133
Ginblock 106
Girder 19, 30, 31, 36, 37, 45, 93
Gironde estuary (lighthouse) 238
Girth band 118
Gland sealing 62
Glass fiber 19
Gloriana 188
Glued 19
Glückauf 161
Goa (lighthouse) 241
Goal-post mast 93
Go(ing) about 247
Going alongside 253
Going large 246
Gokstad ship 18, 26, 42
Golden Hind 64

Golfito (lighthouse) 240
Gooseneck bolt 82
Gooseneck fitting 93
Goose-winged sail 251
Gorge (bone bait holder) 172
Göta River boat 128
Gouge 34, 35
Governor 229
Grand Banks 173
Grand Canary Island (lighthouse) 241
Grapnel 55
Grasshopper engine 153
Gravity davit 66
Great barracuda 180
Great Britain, flag 135
Great cabin 40
Great Eastern 160
Great Harry 64
Great Ormes Head (lighthouse) 240, 241
Great Sambas River 241
Great Western 160
Greece 134
Greek boats 18
Greek fishing boat 173
Greek Periples 242
Greek warship 148
Greenland whale 180
Grenade 207
Grifo Island (lighthouse) 240
Grinnell, Ninturn & Co. 136
Grip oar 149
Grip rope 141
Gripe 20, 21, 32, 33, 66
Grommet 207
Ground line 178
Grängesberg-Oxelösund, Trafik AB 49
Guadalcanal Island (lighthouse) 241
Guafo Island (lighthouse) 240
Guantánamo (lighthouse) 240
Guard ring propeller 155
Guaymas 240
Gudgeon 44, 45
Gudgeon strap 42, 43
Guided missile 212, 220, 221
Gun 60, 206, 210, 211, 212
Gun balancing gear 212
Gunboat 207
Gun carriage 207
Gun deck beam 32, 40
Gun elevation 217
Gun ladle 207
Gunport 40
Gunport lid 51
Gun tackle 123
Gun with accessories 207

LIST OF SOURCES

AB. Allhems Förlag
SVENSKA FLOTTANS HISTORIA. *Malmö 1942—1945.*
Ashley, Clifford W.
THE ASHLEY BOOK OF KNOTS. *New York 1944.*
Babcock & Wilcox
MARINE STEAM. *New York 1928.*
Bartlews
YOUR NEW BOAT. *London 1947.*
Beck, Stuart E.
THE SHIP — HOW SHE WORKS. *Southampton 1955.*
Bergström, C. A.
FARTYGSMASKINER. *Stockholm 1934.*
Bernung, Holm, Petersson, Tegnér
SJÖMANSKAP. *Göteborg 1959.*
Blomgren, Axel S.
SJÖMANSKAP. *Göteborg 1948.*
AB. Bofors
BOFORS. *Göteborg 1958.*
Bonwick, George J.
SEAMANSHIP HANDBOOK. *Liverpool 1952.*
Branch, W. J. V. och Brook-Williams, E.
A SHORT HISTORY OF NAVIGATION. *Annapolis 1942.*
Burmeister & Wain
THE SHIPYARDS OF BURMEISTER & WAIN LTD.
Köpenhamn 1929.
Chapman af, F. H.
ARCHITECTURA NAVALIS MERCATORIA. *Stockholm 1768.*
Classon, Edward och Franzén, Anders
WASA — FYND OCH BÄRGNING. *Stockholm 1959.*
Collinder, Per
FRÅN NOAKS DUVA TILL GYROKOMPASSEN. *Stockholm 1943.*
Crouch, H. F.
NUCLEAR SHIP PROPULSION. *Cambridge 1960.*
Dana, R. H.
TWO YEARS BEFORE THE MAST. *London 1875.*
Dodman, Frank E.
THE OBSERVER'S BOOK OF SHIPS. *London 1961.*
Dugan, James
THE GREAT IRON SHIP. *London 1953.*
Engström, Ivar A.
LÄROBOK I SKEPPSBYGGERI. *Stockholm 1924.*
Evans, I. O.
THE OBSERVER'S BOOK OF FLAGS. *London 1959.*
Forshell, Hans
MINAN I SJÖKRIGET. *Stockholm 1959.*
Föreningen Sveriges Sjöfartsmuseum i Stockholm
ÅRSBOK 1943. *Lund 1944.*
Försvarets Kommandoexpedition
ÖRLOGSBOKEN, SJÖMANSINSTRUKTION FÖR FLOTTAN.
Stockholm 1961.
GKSS
PROGRAM FÖR MARSTRANDSREGATTAN. *Göteborg 1962.*
AB. Götaverken
PUBLICATION NO. 389. *Stockholm 1951.*
Handels og Søfartsmuseet på Kronborg
ÅRBOG 1960.
Hansen, G.
LAEREBOG I SKIBSBYGNING OG SKIBSKONSTRUKTION.
Köpenhamn 1909.
Hardy, A. C.
HAVSFISKE I HELA VÄRLDEN. *Malmö 1947.*
MODERN MARINE ENGINEERING. VOL. II. *London 1948.*
THE BOOK OF THE SHIP. *London 1948.*
Hasslöf, Olof
SVENSKA VÄSTKUSTFISKARNA. *Stockholm 1947.*

Henschke, W.
SCHIFFBAUTECHNISCHES HANDBUCH, BAND IV. *Berlin 1958.*
Her Majesty's stationary office
MANUAL OF SEAMANSHIP. *I, II and III. London 1951.*
Hewson, J.
A HISTORY OF THE PRACTICE OF NAVIGATION. *Glasgow 1951.*
Hägg, Erik
UNDER TRETUNGAD FLAGGA. *Stockholm 1941.*
UNDER SEGEL. *Stockholm 1943.*
Imray, Laurie, Norie & Wilson Ltd.
LIGHTS AND TIDES OF THE WORLD. *London 1961.*
Kannik, Preben
FLAGGOR I FÄRG FRÅN HELA VÄRLDEN.
Köpenhamn and Stockholm 1957.
Kerchove, René de
INTERNATIONAL MARITIME DICTIONARY. *New York 1948.*
Kierkegaard, N. C.
PRAKTISK SKEPPSBYGGNADSKONST. *Göteborg 1864.*
Kungl. Kommerskollegium, Sjöfartsbyrån
INTERNATIONELL SIGNALBOK. *Stockholm 1931.*
Laas, W.
DIE GROSSEN SEGELSCHIFFE (IHRE ENTWICKLUNG
UND ZUKUNFT). *Berlin 1908.*
Lammeren, Van
RESISTAS PROPULSION AND STEERING OF SHIPS.
Haarlem 1948.
Landström, Björn
SKEPPET. *Weert 1961.*
Laughlin Co.
CATALOGUE NO. 75. *Portland 1912.*
Lehmann, Johannes
BURMEISTER & WAIN GENNEM HUNDREDE AAR.
Köpenhamn 1943.
Linder, Wilhelm
LÄROBOK I SJÖMANSKAP. *Stockholm 1896.*
Lindström, Claes
SJÖFARTENS HISTORIA. *Stockholm 1951.*
Lisle, B.
TANKER TECHNIQUE 1700—1936. *London 1936.*
Lubbock, Basil
THE CHINA CLIPPERS. *Glasgow 1946.*
THE WESTERN OCEAN PACKETS. *Glasgow 1925.*
THE LAST OF THE WINDJAMMERS. *Glasgow 1927.*
Lundmark, Efraïm
REDERI SVEA. *Stockholm 1951.*
Magnus, Olaus
HISTORIA OM DE NORDISKA FOLKEN. *Uppsala 1909—1951.*
Marinstabens utbildningsavd.
ÖRLOGSFARTYG OCH MARINA VAPEN. *Uppsala 1961.*
Middendorf, F.
BEMASTUNG UND TAKELUNG DER SCHIFFE. *Leipzig 1903.*
Natur och Kultur
DET SVENSKA ATOMARBETET. *Stockholm 1958.*
Nilsson, N. G. and Åsbrink, G.
SVERIGES SJÖFART. *Stockholm 1921.*
Nordisk Familjeboks Förlag
NORDISK FAMILJEBOK. *Stockholm 1904—1926.*
Paasch, H.
FROM KEEL TO TRUCK. *Antwerpen 1885.*
MARINE ENCYKLOPEDIA. *Antwerpen 1885.*
Parker, H. and Bowen, F. C.
MAIL AND PASSENGER STEAMSHIPS OF THE 19TH CENTURY.
London 1928.
Radcliffe, William
FISHING FROM THE EARLIEST TIMES. *London 1921.*

Rooij, G. de
PRACTICAL SHIPBUILDING A. *Haarlem 1961.*
Rålamb, Åke Classon
SKEPS BYGGERIJ ELLER ADELIG ÖFNINGS TIONDE TOM.
Stockholm 1691 and Malmö 1943.
Röding, J.H.
ALLGEMEINES WÖRTERBUCH DER MARINE. *Hamburg 1798.*
Schiøtz, Eyvind
JEG ER SEJLER. *Köpenhamn 1959.*
Seaton, A. E.
THE MANUAL OF MARINE ENGINEERING. *London 1904.*
Smith, Edgar C.
A SHORT HISTORY OF NAVAL AND MARINE ENGINEERING.
Cambridge 1938.
Sohlmans Förlag
SOHLMANS SJÖLEXIKON. *Örebro 1935.*
BOKEN OM HAVET. *Stockholm 1950.*
Strömberg, C. A.
INGENJÖRSHANDBOKEN, *del II. Stockholm 1948.*
Sullivan, Edw.
YACHTING. *London 1894.*
Svenska Lloyd
REDERIAKTIEBOLAGET SVENSKA LLOYD. *Göteborg 1920.*
Svensson, Sam
LÄROBOK I SJÖMANSKAP. *Stockholm 1959.*
SEGEL GENOM SEKLER. *Amsterdam 1961.*
Traung, Olof
UR SJÖFARTENS HÄVDER — EN VANDRING GENOM
SJÖFARTSMUSEET. *Göteborg 1933.*
Tuxen, J. S.
SJÖFARTEN OG SKIBSBYGNINGSKUNSTEN. *Köpenhamn 1879.*
Uggla, C. L.
AFHANDLING UTI SKEPPSBYGGERI TILL NAVIGATIONS-
SKOLORNAS TJENST. *Göteborg 1856.*
Underhill, Harold A.
MASTING AND RIGGING THE CLIPPER SHIPS AND OCEAN
CARRIER. *Glasgow 1946.*
SAILING SHIP RIGS AND RIGGING. *Glasgow 1938.*
Unger, Gunnar
ILLUSTRERAD SVENSK SJÖKRIGSHISTORIA. *Stockholm 1909.*
United States Naval Academy
NAVAL TURBINES. *Annapolis 1955.*
Weber, I. C.
FRA HJULSKIBENES DAGE. *Köpenhamn 1919.*
Webster, F. B.
SHIPBUILDING CYKLOPEDIA. *New York 1920.*
Wedge, Philip L.
FLAGS AND FUNNELS. *Glasgow 1958.*
Whitaker, H. E.
BRITISH AND INTERNATIONAL RACING YACHT CLASSES.
London 1954.
Witt, G. C.
PRAKTISK OCH THEORETISK HANDLEDNING I SKEPPS-
BYGGERI MED SÄRSKILD TILLÄMPNING PÅ HANDELSFARTYG.
Stockholm 1863.
Åhlund, G. B.
HANDBOK I ARTILLERI FÖR FLOTTAN, SJÖARTILLERIETS
GRUNDER. *Stockholm 1951.*

Periodicals
MARINE ENGINEER
NATIONAL GEOGRAPHIC MAGAZINE
SCHIFFBAU
VEREIN DEUTSCHE INGENIEURE
SVENSK SJÖFARTS TIDNING